DAUGHTER OF VALDORO

D0424626

Evelyn Stewart Armstrong

Daughter of Valdoro

Edited by Lesley Saxby

Futura Publications Limited

A Futura Book

First published in Great Britain in 1974
by Macdonald & Jane's
(Macdonald & Co (Publishers) Ltd)
First Futura Publications edition 1975
(Reprinted 1977, 1978)
Copyright © Evelyn Stewart Armstrong 1974

This book is sold subject to the condition
that it shall not, by way of trade or
otherwise, be lent, re-sold, hired out or
otherwise circulated without the publisher's
prior consent in any form of binding or
cover other than that in which it is
published and without a similar condition
including this condition being imposed on the
subsequent purchaser.

ISBN 0 8600 71839

Printed in Great Britain by
C. Nicholls & Company Ltd
The Philips Park Press
Manchester

Futura Publications Ltd
110 Warner Road
LONDON SE5

CHAPTER ONE

'The man couldn't be worse! He's a lecher and a murderer, and he's coming here!' The voice was sharp with hatred and disgust. 'It's monstrous!'

Elena looked up calmly from her work. It did no good to be so vehement, she thought, although the statement might well be true.

The shutters at the tall windows were almost closed; between them the sunlight, a bar of mote-flecked gold, fell on the floor in front of the desk at which she sat.

She could hear the pad of feet on the courtyard outside; the *peones* had been told to carry on with their work as usual, but no doubt a few of them had made some excuse to visit old Pedro in the stables, and were hanging about in the hope of catching a first sight of the man who had roused such a violent antipathy in Cristina.

And now Cristina was drumming with her fingers on the desk top, impatient for some remark in support of her own feelings.

'Well, say something, Elena!'

They had never seen him; the newspapers they had been allowed to read had naturally been in total opposition; but one could hardly condemn the man out of hand, no matter how black the case seemed against him.

'He's a general. Whether that makes him a murderer depends on your point of view, I suppose.'

'Don't you *know*, Elena? They say he even shoots his own men if he feels like it! And as for his reputation with women, no one's safe with him!'

It wasn't his morals, Elena thought, but his methods which concerned her; his methods of Land Reform, and in particular,

1

how he applied the Sequestration Law.

'I don't *know* anything. I've *heard* an awful lot. With stories as conflicting as those told about the General it's best to keep an open mind.'

'Oh, I shall never understand you! An open mind after all he's done to us. After Luis — and Vicente!'

'Be reasonable, Cristina. Luis wasn't killed in one of the General's battles; and as for Vicente — well, who knows?'

Cristina tossed back her dark chestnut hair in a gesture of contempt.

'Yes, and who caused the Revolution? Our beloved President!' The words were heavy with irony and hatred. 'And who won all the battles for him? The General! Revolution!' she added bitterly. 'Just another South American revolution! But it's our lives he's ruining. He kills our men, and now he's going to beggar us!'

'We've got to accept things as they are. The law has been passed.'

Elena couldn't help sounding stubborn; one must face facts.

'And what's to become of us? Just when I was thinking that things couldn't possibly be any worse, they tell us that this — this monster is coming here! Why should we have to endure it?' She paused as another thought struck her. 'I wonder what he will be like? Some filthy half-breed Indian who'll suck his teeth and spit on the carpets, for all we know!'

'He can't be quite like that. Surely the President, who is at least a man of education, would choose men of intelligence and passable behaviour to be his ministers.'

'That brute was cunning enough to win his battles. Now Gonzalez is President he gets his reward. Being a general doesn't satisfy him, he has to have a prize. The Ministry of Land Reform! How can you sit there so calmly? Today he's coming to look at one of the richest pickings, to turn it over and see what it's worth to *him* — your own estate Valdoro!'

Elena bent her head as if studying the ledger. 'Please, Mother of God, don't let it be like that,' she prayed. 'Don't let him take Valdoro. The law has been passed. Much of the estate

2

will have to go; let him leave us something. The house, some land, so that we can still feel we belong here.'

Valdoro. For three years she had lived for the *estancia*; the successive blows that had struck her had only left her this one love.

She had been born here, it was part of the fibre of her being. It was her only home. The town house in Varena, the villa on the coast — they had had their uses when she was younger. So had the finishing school in Brazil, and the university; they had given her good years. But Valdoro was different.

The house had been built by the first Moural to come to Riqueza from Spain. It had sheltered each successive generation; in its stable court dozens of tiny Mourales had been lifted on to their first ponies; its rolling lands had seen them ride further and further afield as they grew older and stronger, until the great *pampa* itself was their playground.

Then came the Revolution. It had hit them hard, and yet in some strange way perhaps it had helped her. For her troubles had started before then: they had started when she hadn't been allowed to marry Vicente.

Until that time, apart from her interest in the horses, she had played no part in the estate management. Later her father had encouraged her to help him, thinking it might take her mind off the unfortunate affair.

When the Revolution broke and her father died, her brother Luis had been glad she knew so much. And when he, too, was gone, it was hard work alone that could dull the sharpness of sorrow. She had forced herself into acceptance, even of Vicente's death; it was not the apathy of resignation but the stoic calm of a resolve to find something worthwhile to live for.

'If our workers had any loyalty one of them would shoot him in the back! But I suppose, like all the common folk, they'll make an idol of him.'

What was Cristina talking about? Oh, yes, the General. He would be here soon.

3

'I hope no one thinks of it. It would cause a great deal of bother. And we must try not to antagonize him, for our own sakes.'

He was probably a boor and a blackguard, but she would accept him, she'd speak him fair, even treat him as an equal. She must, for the sake of Valdoro. Someone had to do it. Her mother would not. But her mother was only a Moural by marriage, and for all her pride she was a de Zurga. Valdoro was not in her heart, it was outside her, a thing of status. But she, Elena, was her father's daughter, and 'La Hija de Valdoro'.

It was a great thing, to be the Daughter of Valdoro, and without sacrificing her dignity she would do all she could to keep her place there.

But against such a man as the General, what could one do?

The road from Varena was baking under the summer sun. The jeep had been travelling since early morning, and it had met little traffic; a few vehicles, mostly military, in the capital, some farm carts on the outskirts bringing produce into market, a lorry or two. And then the macadam was finished, there was not a building in sight, and the dirt road lay like a pale fawn ribbon between the green coffee plantations.

The road climbed steadily, and the escorting truck had dropped a little distance behind to avoid in some degree the cloud of dust which billowed up behind the jeep.

The two men in the jeep said nothing. The driver, in the rough uniform of a soldier in the Riquezan Army, a sergeant's stripes on his sleeve, kept his eyes on the road and tried to ignore the dryness of his throat.

Beside him the officer, whose uniform excellent in quality and cut showed signs of high rank and a devoted batman, sat with his eyes closed, apparently half asleep. But the sergeant was not deceived: this probably meant that the brain under the lazily tilted cap was extremely active. Was he thinking of Valdoro?

Valdoro. That had once been a name to conjure with. When one said it there was the taste on the tongue of nobility and

4

the hidalgo tradition. Though in Spain the hidalgo was the lowest grade of nobleman, in Riqueza the word had a different significance.

Two centuries ago, on hearing that the lands of South America were rich fruit ripe for the picking, an ambitious few had banded together and, taking their families with them, had plucked Riqueza from the New World and kept it for their own. They had divided it between them, sharing the wealth, the land, the power; they were the rulers and the only aristocrats. The families intermarried, and each union was a diplomatic alliance. They kept the old ways, the old traditions. But inevitably they over-reached themselves.

It was the consuming desire of most of the aristocrats to keep all the power and wealth to themselves which had caused the Revolution. Now they were being stripped of everything they valued. Of their vast estates, their wealth, their power, their pride, what would be left to them? Only their pride, it seemed.

Past the plantations, still climbing, into the maize districts, the Rio Oro still in sight over to their right, a broad silver ribbon whose waters they followed for many miles.

Ah, but it was lovely country, thought Gregor Marint. Country in which a man could stretch and breathe. Rolling land, well-grassed, with a sprinkling of trees, the river well below them now, and running smaller and swifter.

Valdoro had been a fine name before the Revolution. But now — what was he going to find? An *estancia* inhabited by three women. All that land — all that cattle, the blood-stock, the plantations, everything — and three women. Three women alone there for a couple of years or more! *Dios*, it would be in one hell of a state! Rack and ruin, everything mismanaged and neglected.

Still, that was a very good reason for coming here. Easy jobs didn't interest him; he'd always thrived on the difficult ones. He'd show what State management could do. The more run down the place was, the more room for reorganization. In a few years he'd make a model State Farm of it.

They'd left Puenterojo three quarters of an hour ago, they should be able to see the house any moment now. They rounded a bend and there it was in the distance, set up on higher ground commanding the shallow rift which opened out on to the broad *pampa*, sheltered by a wooded slope from the cold winds which would blow in winter.

As the jeep lurched along the intervening miles Gregor Marint, with the trained eye of a soldier who had fought his way through many a building, interested himself in speculating on the layout of Valdoro house.

It would be built with a main block and three wings, like a capital E. The E was lying on its back, and the house front that faced the road would be the back of the E. The three arms would enclose two courtyards. One would be a garden court, a Spanish-style patio, around which the main rooms would be grouped. The other – yes, he could just see that the drive curved to the right through an archway – would lead to a courtyard flanked by garages and stables, backed by the servants' wing.

Now he could really see the house. The long façade, two storeys high, spread itself in a great expanse of white walls and violet-painted window shutters. Stone built – *por Dios*, that Moural had some money! Maybe he had his own stone quarry in the foothills – nothing was impossible! Unlimited cheap labour in those days, of course.

There was even a low stone wall fronting the road and running back on either side; this had been built for appearance, to be a fitting setting for the pair of magnificent wrought-iron gates which closed off the entrance drive.

The jeep pulled up, for the great gates were shut, and no one appeared to open them. They needn't tell him he wasn't welcome. He knew. The sergeant opened the gates, returned to the jeep, and they began to mount the long drive.

Luisa, Condesa de Valdoro, descended the broad staircase into the main hall of the house. She was an impressive woman, of handsome patrician appearance, and carried herself with every

6

indication of pride and authority. She knew she was infinitely superior to this upstart she was obliged to entertain – a common soldier who wasn't fit to set his boots inside her walls. A general! They didn't make such rubbish into officers before the Revolution. It was an insult to the officer class. He had come up from nothing, by stepping on the bodies of dead officers of good birth. It was revolting to think of it.

Many of the friends of her family had been Army officers, but in those days one had to have birth and breeding, as well as money, to get a commission; it was a good life for a younger son who had no estate responsibilities. The private soldiers were the lowest of the low, but they could fight with a man of breeding to direct them, if there was fighting to be done. And when there was no fighting they knew their place. They didn't dream of being officers, they knew it was beyond their capabilities, quite apart from other considerations.

What must the Army be like now? Just a rabble of legalized robbers, with the biggest robber at the head. Minister of Land Reform they called him. Minister of Land Grabbing they meant.

A stout middle-aged woman came bustling out of the door leading from the servants' quarters. 'Condesa! Condesa! The General! They have seen the cars, Pedro says, on the road. He will be here any minute!'

'Then find the señoritas at once, Carmela. They must be here with me when he arrives.'

As she waited, Luisa Moural gazed round the huge room with malicious satisfaction. That jumped-up *peón* ought to be thoroughly ill at ease: he'd probably gone from an adobe hut to a barracks, and knew nothing else until he'd been made a Minister. How would he feel in a place like this?

The room was very large, and beautifully proportioned. The white walls were panelled to shoulder height, the floor laid with polished tiles. At one end, round a vast fireplace, were grouped two settees and several armchairs upholstered in heavy damask. The broad chimney breast bore the eighteenth-century portrait of a Spanish nobleman, the founder of

7

Valdoro.

His fine aquiline features, composed in an expression of great dignity and pride, could be clearly traced in the softened feminine beauty of her own daughter.

The portrait was flanked by a pair of antique duelling pistols, most handsome weapons; they had been her late husband's pride — she had often seen him demonstrate to guests that they were extremely accurate, and in as good condition as when they were first fired.

To one side of the room was an outsize dining-table which gleamed from the polishing of generations of servants, surrounded by carved chairs upholstered in leather. Beautiful cabinets stood against the walls. There were bookcases, a dower chest, and an antique gaming table. The floor was strewn with handwoven rugs, and there were flowers everywhere; their scent hung on the air.

This was her house, the setting for her nobility. She'd make the General realize that.

She sat down on a sofa by the fireplace and motioned the girls to join her as they came into the room.

Elena did not see the gesture. She stood, holding her slim body very straight, staring at the door through which the General would enter.

For a moment Elena held her breath. Then the door at the far end of the room swung open.

He certainly wasn't Cristina's 'half-breed Indian'. His skin was deeply tanned, but it had no coppery tinge; his hair was dark brown, not coarse and black, not even the fine black of the Spanish-Riquezan, as was her own.

She was aware that the light khaki uniform fitted smoothly over wide shoulders and powerful chest, a spare waist and hips; the breadth was not fleshiness but muscle and big bones. His face — she looked long and coolly at his face. A broad forehead, straight dark brows, deep-set eyes — what colour? — not black; a short nose, a strong jaw, a mouth that on anyone else she would have called generous, with a well-chiselled top lip pressed firmly into a full lower one.

8

She could not judge his age – not less than thirty, but not more than forty, she thought.

He addressed himself to Doña Luisa, giving her a brief military salute. 'Señora Mo ural?'

Doña Luisa rose, and replied with icy precision: 'I am the Condesa de Valdoro.'

You have abolished titles, thought Elena, but you can't prevent my mother from using hers.

He ignored the implied correction. 'I am General Marint. And these young ladies?'

Doña Luisa indicated each with a gesture. 'My daughter, and my god-daughter, Señorita de Burgos.'

She had the hidalga's facility at giving a subtle but unmistakable snub, volunteering no first names as he would, of course, never be allowed the familiarity of their use. He gave them each a brief nod and a quick keen glance.

'Then let's get down to business.'

Though he did not speak with aristocratic precision his accent was not uncultured, and his voice had a resonance that heightened the impression of strength and masculinity. His personality was clashing across their feminine household like a trumpet breaking into a trio of violins.

He sat down at the head of the table, obliging them to join him. Doña Luisa seated herself to one side, three places down, so that when Elena sat next to her and Cristina opposite there were still empty chairs on either side of him. He was being politely ostracized.

The soldier, who had been standing to attention a few paces away, came forward and handed him a document case. The General spoke to him.

'See that the men get something to eat and drink, and sign for it, Sergeant. If there's wine available they can have their dinner ration. Find my room and get my bags up there, then stay with the men until I send for you.'

The sergeant snapped a salute and marched out.

Well, thought Elena, he keeps his men up to scratch, it seems.

9

He was speaking again, and having taken some papers from the briefcase, was offering one to her mother.

'Señora Moural, by order of the Government, under the new Land Reform Laws, your estate of Valdoro has been confiscated. Here is the Order of Sequestration.'

Doña Luisa took it, glanced at it, and laid it back on the table.

'I do not recognize your government, and I consider its laws invalid. I shall fight this.'

She ignored the hand which Elena placed gently on her arm.

The General leaned back in his chair. 'You'd better consider that carefully. Litigation is expensive, especially against the Government, and I doubt whether you'll have money to spare for such luxuries.'

'That is my affair.'

'In any case, the sequestration order will be carried out as soon as practicable. You may not know that the bulk of your money in the bank also comes under this order. All accounts are frozen at present except for a living allowance, and that state of affairs will continue. Meanwhile, I shall be assessing the estate. I had better explain what that will mean to you.'

'Please do,' remarked Doña Luisa acidly.

'I have to find out just what this estate consists of, in land and stock, how it is being used, and what its potentials are. *You* are going to be assessed too, in terms of how much money you have taken from the estate and how much you have put back in, in every way — wages, workers' living quarters, improvements, re-stocking, and so forth. I shall require all the records you have over the past four years.'

He paused, looking at her shrewdly. 'I hope you've kept records. Some landowners seem to consider it beneath their dignity to commit anything concerning money to paper. Any records you have it will be in your best interests to produce, otherwise I shall have to make arbitrary judgements. Without documents these are hardly likely to be in your favour. Is that clear?'

'Perfectly.'

Elena's mouth was dry. She felt rather sick. If they were going to be penniless, how would her mother, used to luxury, manage to live in poverty?

'Now for a few details. You will be given some compensation according to how well the estate has been run. In other words, an owner who has taken everything and given nothing back will get virtually nothing. If you've been ploughing back some profits you'll get some financial rebate out of your confiscated funds.'

He glanced about him. 'Now to the house. The Government has the rights over it as well, in case it may be of use to us. If we don't want it, you are free to buy it back, plus a fixed amount of land around it. The contents remain yours in either case.'

For a moment Doña Luisa was speechless.

'Buy back my own house!' she burst out at last. 'Your insolence is only equalled by your rapacity! In the face of that I'm surprised you even leave me my furniture!'

'It's not my decision, Señora Moural. If it were, I might consider some of this stuff worth expropriating.'

Was he baiting her?

'And how am I supposed to live, without capital or income?'

'There is a land allowance, and you'll have some capital left, if you don't do anything silly. By the way, don't forget I have access to all bank records. As for living, some of you could try working. It would be a change for you, no doubt, but there are people who do it all their lives.'

Elena's heart began pounding unpleasantly. They could not afford to antagonize this man, but she knew her mother would not take such remarks without retaliating. She prayed that her mother would practise some restraint.

Doña Luisa spoke with a voice as smooth as silk. 'Just one thing, General.'

'Yes?'

'How much am I expected to offer you to ensure

11

favourable consideration?'

Dios! thought Elena. True or not, he'll squeeze us dry for that imputation. She gazed at the General, but his face betrayed nothing.

When he spoke his voice was hard but level. 'Señora Moural, what you think of me is of no importance. But take this warning. If I hear of anyone under my orders accepting bribes they will be severely dealt with. But that will be nothing to the punishment whoever bribed them will get. Is that understood?'

Doña Luisa eyed him defiantly. 'I would remind you that we are not under martial law now. I doubt if you can punish a civilian for such a thing.'

'Don't put it to the test. I give the orders here, to everyone, without exception. If you accept that and do as you're told everything will go smoothly. If you try to fight me, openly or behind my back, I shall break you.'

Then, most surprisingly, Cristina found her voice. 'Do you think we care what you do, after what you've done already? How can you come here, ordering us about, wearing a revolver and jingling that collection of bloodstained ironmongery — ' Her voice broke off, she was choking with anger.

The General laughed. 'Now, if we've all had our joke we'll conclude our business for this morning. Señora Moural, will you send for your estate manager. I want to see him at once.'

'I have no estate manager, General Marint,' Doña Luisa replied.

'Then what have you got? A bailiff, a foreman, something or other.'

Suddenly determined, Elena spoke up. 'I have been acting as estate manager for my mother for the past two years.'

The General's dark brows were raised incredulously. 'You? What do you do? Hand out the wages and pick the flowers?'

'You will judge for yourself, no doubt. Why do you want the manager?'

He now looked both surprised and amused. 'To see the records, for a start.'

Elena rose. I'll shake his male superiority, she thought.

'Then if you will come with me to the office I will show you. Will you excuse us, Mother?'

As she led the way to the office Elena's brain was busy. She knew that they were all on the verge of ruin, and that her mother, blinded by hate and pride, would do nothing to help matters. She still seemed to think that destitution would never come to the Mourales, that they would be saved if necessary by some divine intervention. Cristina was too emotional to be of any use. No, everything depended on her, as it had done for years.

If only things had been different, if only her parents had let her marry Vicente he might still be alive, and here to help her. But it had been an unsuitable match; they were bitterly opposed to it. Elena knew she had been right not to press the matter. Elopement would have been her only chance of marriage.

She had never understood Vicente's attitude. He had been as desperately in love with her as she had been with him, and yet he had accepted all the rebuffs. He, who had always stood out so strongly for anything he believed in, made no attempt to fight for her. He had never suggested any alternative.

In any case, elopement would have been out of the question. Her father had a bad heart condition; to shock and anger him so might well cause his death. Some two years before, a marriage had been proposed for her which was not to her liking. Her mother pressed the matter strongly and the rest of the family was in favour. She had had to beg her father not to let the negotiations continue.

He had promised her that he would never urge her to marry against her inclinations. The least she could do for him in the circumstances was to accept his ruling about Vicente, and hope that time would alter the case. And time did alter the case, but not as she had hoped.

Six months later the political situation had deteriorated so much that rebellion broke out. This started the Revolution The Army was divided in its allegiance, and in a mutiny at one of the barracks an officer who was her father's dearest friend

13

was killed. Four days after receiving the news he, too, was dead.

Her brother Luis took over the running of the estate. Elena, who had been helping her father, now was able to assist Luis in the shouldering of his responsibilities. And then Luis had got it into his head that he must join the volunteers, and off he went, to be killed in a skirmish a few months later.

Doña Luisa had his body brought home to be buried in the vault of their private chapel next to his father. Yet in her grief she had no sympathy to spare for Elena when, three weeks later, she heard that Vicente, too, was dead; to her it was a punishment Elena had invited by loving where her parents did not approve.

Elena forced her sorrow to the back of her mind, and took over Valdoro completely. She could only live by working so hard that she had no time for thoughts of Vicente, for heartbreak.

She would go to the office after breakfast, and after spending a short while there would be out on her horse supervising all the running of the plantations, the work on the crops, the care of the cattle and the bloodstock.

And always she watched the welfare of the workers. When a baby fell sick 'La Hija' was asked for advice, when a roof leaked 'La Hija' sent the materials for mending it, when a man nearly severed a finger it was 'La Hija' who bound it up and sent him to the doctor at Puenterojo.

Other people took a long siesta in the afternoon; Elena had a brief rest and then started work again, returning only in time to bathe and change for the evening meal. She would go to bed so tired that even her tormented brain could not keep her awake.

And so, in time, the edge of her sorrow dulled, and she was able to face the prospect of life without Vicente. And life without Vicente meant living for Valdoro, the only worthwhile thing left to her.

In the office Elena indicated the rows of files to the General.

14

They were all labelled; he pulled out one or two at random and glanced through them.

She moved to the map on the wall behind the desk. 'This is Valdoro,' she said.

He came and stood beside her, scanning it, weighing up the sheer size of it, the different heights and types of land the territory covered.

Then he turned his head and stared at her. 'What do you do with it?' he asked bluntly.

She suddenly felt a heightening of emotion within her. The keen eyes – they were a strange greenish-brown – were holding her gaze, he was standing close to her, she could smell the faint masculine aroma of tobacco. She forced her attention back to the map.

'Here, in the lower part of the valley, are the coffee plantations. This part running towards the river and Puenterojo is mostly under maize, with some fruit. I can show you detailed charts of all the crops. All this – ' she ran her hand over the higher ground – 'is used for cattle. Here, in the foothills, on the western boundaries of Valdoro, are the vineyards.'

She did not look at him, but she knew when he turned from the map and gazed at her again.

'What's the wine like?'

'Good, we think.'

'How does it travel?'

'Well enough for short distances. Fine for Riqueza, but no good for export.'

He nodded. 'Now, give me some details. What have you been doing in the past two years?'

He listened, assessing everything. She knew what she was talking about. Surprising, that. She was a gorgeous creature. Lovely, not lush. No flamboyance. Hair like polished jet, not piled up in the Spanish fashion the Riquezan society women usually adopted, but coiled low on the nape of her neck, which was slender, graceful, holding the head poised like a flower. Her skin was clear, creamy pink; her mouth soft and

15

red, but not babyish; and that was a determined little chin.

She was telling him how her plans for breeding high quality cattle had been delayed by the internal situation of the country. After some minutes he raised his hand.

'That's all right. I can see you know what you're talking about, in theory at least. You'd be surprised how many people learn up a page or two of a book and try to convince me they're worth ten times the wages they're really earning.'

For a moment Elena was speechless. The man had more subtlety than she gave him credit for. She had not realized that he was testing her knowledge. But here was the opportunity she wanted. She plunged in.

'What happens to the estate workers? Are they employed by the Government now, at their own jobs?'

'Yes, provided they can do what they say they can. I'll need a register of the lot of them.'

'I can give you that.' She handed him the file. 'But I must add my own name.'

'Yours?' he queried, that slightly derisive smile beginning to creep to his lips.

'Yes. I've been working on the *estancia* for three years, why shouldn't I stay? I'm prepared to go on working.'

He gave her a long look. 'I'll register you if you wish. But I can't put you down as estate manager, whatever you think you've been doing.'

'I don't think. I know I've been doing the job, and doing it as well as most men could under the circumstances.'

He leaned forward, his arms on the desk. He was younger than she had thought. And he was laughing at her.

'Now, come, Señorita Moural, let us be realists. No woman could do this job as a man would do it. In some things, yes, if she were as capable as no doubt you are. But you must admit your limitations. You have a very big ranch here; don't tell me that your mama would allow you to go out riding for days on end, sleeping in a poncho on the ground among the men.'

She bit back her fury. He had hit on the one weak spot. Superb horsewoman as she was, she could not cover the range as she would like. With Luis she could, and did, ride with the men, occasionally camping with them on the pampa, but since his death her mother had insisted that she got back to the big house by evening. Thus, since there had been no petrol to spare for the truck, there were some parts of the range she had not been able to visit for nearly three years.

He drew the file towards him. 'I'll register you, but I'll leave your occupation blank at present. Name?"

'Elena Moural.' She was very careful not to add 'de Valdoro'.

'Single, married, or widow? Single. Age?'

'Twenty-four.'

He looked at her quizzically.

'Why should I lie to you about my age?' she asked coldly.

'Why indeed? Women lie about their age to prospective suitors,' was his suave reply.

Elena seethed inwardly. I suppose he means I have no more charm for him than he has for me, she thought.

'Age, twenty-four. Occupation, leave blank. Now, Señorita Moural, be a sensible girl. Forget about this business of wanting a job. Find some agreeable fellow and get married. That shouldn't be difficult!'

How dare he! As if she would marry for convenience, for security! How dare he imply that she was no more than a marketable commodity! The fact was, of course, he found it awkward that the daughter of the *estancia* should apply for a job like any ordinary working girl.

'I see. I'm something of a problem to you, General Marint. Well, I'm not going to solve your problem for you by getting married. I wish to go on working here.'

He shrugged. 'Very well. But I won't guarantee you'll like it.' He put down his pen. 'Before you go I'll check whether I need your information on anything. Your files seem in good order, I'll say that.'

He began to look through some of his own papers. Elena sat and waited, trying not to watch him, but her eyes kept straying back to his downbent head, his broad brown hands.

17

What was so disturbing about this man? The fact that he had so much power over Valdoro — and thus over her life? It could only be that. Or was it just that he was a man? But that was a ridiculous idea, she told herself hotly, she was dealing with men all the time.

Her eyes flicked over him again. Handling her workers was different from this; it was a long time since she had met any man on a footing of social equality, and like it or not, that was how this man must be treated. She glanced at his red tabs and modals, reminding herself that whatever his origins he was a general.

He looked up and she felt herself flushing.

'It seems straightforward. I can make a start,' he told her. 'I shall take over this office for my work. It's convenient, and all the records are here. A lot of the time I shall be outside, of course. Come here for your orders each morning. You will be carrying on with your work as usual for the present, but everything must be reported to me. You can go now, but be here tomorrow sharp at eight o'clock.'

She stood up, gritting her teeth, not trusting herself to reply.

He smiled. 'You don't like it, do you?'

Still she said nothing.

'You don't like being a worker instead of a boss. Taking orders instead of giving them.'

It was too much for her.

'*I* don't give orders in that manner. And I've never before met a general who spoke to me as if I were one of his private soldiers!'

He leaned back and grinned. 'Ah, but you've never before met a general who used to *be* a private soldier! I'm not one of the old school! You'll get no kiss-your-hand courtesies from me. I must make that quite clear.'

She fired her answer back at him. 'You have! With all the persuasive charm of one of your own tanks!'

He threw back his head with a quick laugh. 'Now don't be saucy with me — you'll find it doesn't pay! I've just told you,

I'm not the old officer class, constrained by codes of honour and corsets! If you behave like a cross little girl I'm quite capable of correcting you in the appropriate way.'

Her chin lifted and she gave him her haughtiest look. She wouldn't lower herself to answer him. Was his coarseness deliberate, to annoy her, or did he think he was being funny? The detestable man! If only he would stop grinning at her! The mockery in his eyes would provoke a saint.

And she had intended to be pleasant to him, for the sake of Valdoro. Already that seemed almost impossible. Yet for her mother's sake she must try to put up with him. She allowed herself to give him one more flashing defiant glance as she left the room.

CHAPTER TWO

In the few days since the General's arrival the atmosphere at Valdoro had changed subtly but significantly. Elena, who tried to act as if nothing had altered, was aware of it everywhere. The General might be an unmitigated scoundrel to her mother, but it was plain that the workers liked and respected him on sight, and his men held him in tremendous admiration. Whether it was through affection or discipline there was no denying that a lot of work was being done.

Her mother and Cristina had both been horrified to hear that she intended to continue to work in the estate office, even though it meant at times sharing it with Gregor Marint.

'You know perfectly well, Elena,' her mother said severely, 'that I do not approve of these modern ways. Your father let you attend university against my wishes and, as I expected, you learned contempt for a number of very valuable conventions. When I was a young woman I was never allowed to be alone with a man other than my father or brother. Men are men, and the best of them can be — " she paused delicately — 'indiscreet. But that you should be alone with this ill-bred violent creature! I simply can't allow it.'

'I'm afraid you will have to, Mother,' Elena insisted. 'If we are going to get anything like a fair deal over Valdoro I must settle the clerical work for the estate. But don't worry. He has already told me that most of the time he will be outside, finding out what goes on with the crops and the cattle.'

Doña Luisa compressed her lips disapprovingly, but a streak of indolence and the realization that Elena was working for her benefit made her give up the argument.

Elena had an obsession about Valdoro; she would do what she thought best for the estate. At least, so far, the rogue had not shown any lecherous tendencies. It was unlikely he would risk a scandal with a hidalga's daughter when there were plenty of girls down by the plantations who might well be obliging.

Her mother saw possibilities of trouble where none existed, thought Elena. Gregor Marint was only interested in the estate, and came to the office purely for information. Time would tell how far he could be trusted, she would keep her eyes and ears open.

The General was at least blowing a welcome breeze of organization through the place, and doing much that she had been unable to do. The first thing she had noticed was that the soldiers he had brought with him were not, as the Valdoro women had assumed, a general's bodyguard, but a kind of Pioneer Corps of trained technicians, whose job it was to increase efficiency in many directions.

Elena watched with approval through the office window as the outbuildings were investigated and machinery was brought out and serviced. The two tractors were made fit for use and fuelled up with diesel oil the squad had brought. Valdoro had not seen petrol or fuel oil for more than a year.

Then there were the cars which remained in the garage – a big Dodge truck for cattle and general transport, a Ford station wagon used around the estate as an alternative to horses and for bringing in supplies, and last of all, the elderly Rolls Royce, which the family used for formal outings such as their trips to Varena, were made ready for service.

The electricity plant installed by Don Fernando, Elena's father, was in process of being overhauled. It would be wonderful to have electric light and power again after so long.

'What it is to be a general!' Doña Luisa had sourly remarked. 'We haven't been able to get fuel oil or a mechanic for years, yet that barrack-room bandit has only to raise his little finger and the stuff flows for him and technicians spring out of the earth.'

Elena thought it politic not to remark on the exaggeration, nor to enquire whether her mother intended to avail herself of the electricity when it was restored.

21

Each morning Elena did the paper work required by the General, as quickly and efficiently as she knew how. He had thrown her limitations as an outside foreman in her face, but he would have to acknowledge that she did the office work as well as a male secretary.

Now she had a clear idea of what she wanted to do. Private *estancia* or State Farm, someone would have to be in charge of the clerical work — why not herself?

Her mother, she hoped, would find enough money to retain the Valdoro house, they could go on living there, and if she could persuade the General — if persuade was the word — to give her the office job she could still work at Valdoro and be paid for it.

It wouldn't be the same. She wouldn't have the freedom to ride the pampas, she wouldn't have the direction of the estate, but she would be there; and her salary would mean that she could help her mother by paying her way. To Elena it seemed the best — the only — solution.

Being a general had its advantages, Elena thought. At present she had plenty of cattle, but marketing was difficult — absurdly so, when other parts of the country were crying out for beef. There was nothing she could do about it; she'd tried everything. But Marint had actually arranged for a special cattle train to be run in order to get a large number of their beasts to the Varena market. Rolling stock was so scarce that this was something in the nature of a miracle. Yes, he had his points.

She didn't like him, but she had to admit that he hadn't seriously rubbed her up the wrong way in the last few days. Once or twice he had made a request so abruptly that it was more like an order, and then had added a deliberate '*Por favor,* Señorita Moural,' but there had been more humour than sarcasm in it.

What little time he had spent in the office had gone smoothly, though on more than one occasion she had glanced up and caught him staring at her with a quizzical, appraising

22

look. But there was nothing offensive in this regard – and nothing covert either – he had just gone on looking, and it was Elena who had returned her gaze to the work before her, blushing a little, to her own annoyance.

But this late afternoon Marint was goodness knows where, he had gone off with the jeep, and Elena was riding out to see how the cattle drive was progressing.

As she left the house she could hear a low murmur in the distance; a few minutes' riding and it became distinct, separated into the lowing of cattle and the dull, continuous thud of hooves, pierced now and then by the sharp herding cry of a *vaquero*.

She began to ride in a wide arc in order to skirt the herd. It looked as if the bulk of the cattle was collected and would soon be driven off to Puenterojo for entrainment before nightfall, to travel overnight. It was going well.

The air was full of dust and the noise and smell of cattle; she pulled her neckerchief up over her nose and mouth and gazed over the rolling yellowish-green grassland to where another bunch was being herded in.

She rode towards them, noticing that some of them on the outside of the herd were moving rather slowly and irregularly. She spurred her horse to a canter and looked more closely. One of them was pawing the ground uncertainly; it shook its head and tossed aside a dribble of spittle.

Elena suddenly rose in her stirrups and with the sharp repeated cry of the *vaquero* attempted to stop the bunch. A couple of riders a little way off rode up to help her.

Elena gave a quick order to the man nearest to her, and soon the cattle were being driven back.

Then Elena turned her attention to the two men who were the original drovers; two town boys, fresh out of the Army, who had tried to pass themselves off as *vaqueros* and whom she had taken on, desperate for labour, hoping to make something of them.

Having dealt with them she wheeled her horse again and rode back to the main herd. She knew she had hours of hard

23

work ahead of her; she also knew that the General was too far afield for her to contact him, and that the beasts could not be entrained at Puenterojo that evening.

It was dark before she returned to the big house. She felt as if she were covered in caked dust and perspiration; she had never felt so filthy. She walked wearily from the stables, beating the dust out of her wide-brimmed hat against her breeches.

She crossed the courtyard and went straight to the kitchen. Carmela raised eyes and hands in horror.

'Bring up lots of coffee to my room, Carmela, there's an angel. I'm going to have a long bath.'

It was some time later when the General returned. He bellowed for Carmela, who rushed out from the kitchen to find him striding up and down in a towering rage.

'I'll bring your supper right away in the small dining-room, General!' she gasped.

'To hell with my supper! Fetch Señorita Moural.'

'But, General, she's upstairs, washing her hair.'

'I don't care if she's naked! Tell her to come down at once. If she's not here in three minutes I shall go up.'

Carmela scuttled off like a hen startled by a snake.

Elena had bathed and washed her hair and, clad in underclothes and dressing-gown, was towelling her head when Carmela wheezed out her message.

'And, Señorita, he is furious! He says that if you do not go down in three minutes, he will come up.'

Elena seized a pair of trousers and thrust her legs into them. Marint had no scruples, he would be a man of his word, she thought. But what a state she was in! She grabbed a hairbrush and with a few brisk strokes smoothed her damp and disordered hair back from her face, then wound it up turban fashion in a dry towel. She dared not stop for more.

In the small dining-room the General was kicking at the logs in the fireplace. He swung round as she entered.

'So you've started your tricks already, have you?' he said with controlled fury. 'You've picked the wrong man!'

24

Elena looked at him questioningly.

'You know what I'm talking about. Why were the cattle not sent to Puenterojo? Arrangements were made and my orders were clear. I was told you'd countermanded them.'

'And you weren't told why?'

'No. The fellow I spoke to didn't seem to know. I'm asking you.'

'Then I'll tell you. It was because I refuse to sell infected cattle for you or anyone else, General Marint.'

'*Infected cattle*? Nonsense! The ones I saw were perfectly healthy!'

'I hope they are. The main herd was collected and ready to move out when I saw another bunch being driven up. They were sick. I know 'foot and mouth' when I see it I just managed to stop them joining the main herd, and had them sent back and penned well away. They were a bunch which had been on their own, luckily, but I couldn't risk the possibility that there might be some sick cattle in the main herd, so I examined the lot.'

'You *what*?'

'With two or three of the men. We passed them through and looked over them: we couldn't do more than that, of course. But it was a long job, and there was no hope of sending them to Puenterojo before nightfall. It was dark by the time we'd finished; we were using flares by then.'

'I see.' He nodded slowly. 'And you checked every beast between you?'

'Yes.'

'Well, you're not such a bad estate manager, after all.'

'About the sick ones —'

He cut her short. 'We'll discuss that in the office tomorrow. Business is over for tonight.' Suddenly he smiled. 'I'm sorry I was in such a bad temper. I thought you'd been trying a bit of sabotage behind my back.'

'I don't sabotage Valdoro,' she said coldly.

There was a knock on the door and Carmela slipped in, put a tray on the table and hurried out again.

'Then show there's no ill-will. Stay and talk to me for a few minutes.'

This was ridiculous. It was bad enough to have to appear like this, but to be asked to stay and talk . . .

'But I was — '

'Drying your hair. I know. Finish it off here.'

He bent, moved a stool to the front of the fire, and threw on another log.

Elena stood, irresolute.

'Oh, take that off your head. You look like an Arab who's lost his camel.'

He actually untwined the towel from her head and threw it over the back of a chair. She gave in, sat on the stool and shook her hair out to the blaze. He drew an armchair up and sat facing her.

'You'd better have your supper,' she said.

If he would only eat, and not look at her, she would feel less uncomfortable.

'In a minute. Let us talk.'

His calm stare made Elena acutely self-conscious. But why should she be? she thought rebelliously. He wasn't. Anyone would think he watched a woman dry her hair every day of his life.

She did not look at him, but pulled her hair off her shoulders towards the fire. She was very much aware of him, and he was still the General though he now wore a plain khaki shirt and slacks. They had not seen his uniform with the decorations and badges of rank since the day of the official take-over, but it made no difference. He could be just as intimidating. Yet in spite of this odd situation, now that his rage was gone he was not intimidating, she realized with some surprise.

'How is it?' he asked, then reached out and ran his fingers through the length of her black tresses. Still more surprised, she glanced up.

'Fairly dry,' he went on.

Then his hand twined in the hair behind her head and held

26

fast, making her lift her head and look into his eyes.

'What happened to your lover?' he asked.

Elena was dumbfounded.

'Why — who — 'she stammered.

'Oh, no one's been gossiping. I worked it out myself.'

He paused, let go of her hair, leaned back and looked at her coolly, appraisingly, with the suspicion of a smile.

'It was easy. You're young, beautiful, intelligent, but old enough to have been marriageable before the Revolution. You must have had the pick of the young bloods. And you've got the poise that only comes to a woman when she's had a man of her own. But you're not married. So — what happened to your lover?'

Anger began to rise within her, tightening her throat. She stood up.

'Where are you going?'

'Upstairs. I'm under your orders for work, but socially I don't have to put up with your impertinence.'

'Impertinence!' He laughed. 'I was paying you a compliment. And if you go now, I shall think you're a prude.'

'I'm not a prude. But it happens to be my personal affair.'

He patted the stool. 'Come on, then, sit down. I'm not asking you who he was.' She did so, not quite knowing why. 'Of course you've had a lover. Do you take me for an absolute fool?'

His lips smiled mockingly. She threw her hair back and clasped her hands over her knees.

'I see no reason why you should question me about my . . . life.'

'Don't you? Then I'll tell you. Because you're going to belong to me, and when you do I shall prefer to know I'm not taking another man's woman.'

The smile just hovered on his lips, the greenish-brown eyes looked deep into hers. She felt a wave of shock run through her, the pulse in her throat began to throb.

'You're quite incredible!' she gasped. 'How dare you speak to me like that!'

27

He said nothing, but smiled more, and that long dimple crept into his cheek.

'You're just taking advantage of your position!' she flared at him.

'Of course I am! I wouldn't risk trying to make love to you if I were a tuppenny-ha'penny clerk or a private soldier. You'd give me a flea in my ear. But you can't expect me not to use a weapon that's in my hand. I warned you not to expect chivalry from me.'

Elena began to laugh. She was tired, shocked, and unsure of herself. What a conversation this was — and this man didn't think it at all unusual! She went on laughing, holding her face in her hands.

'Here, drink it up.'

He was offering her a cup of coffee. She stopped laughing and drank, trying to get a grip on herself. He took the cup and put it on the hearth.

'You still haven't answered me. What happened to him? Did he stop pleasing you?'

'He died over two years ago,' she answered flatly.

'I see. And there's been no one since?'

'No.'

'Then it's time there was.'

'I don't want anyone else. I loved him.'

'Love! Don't talk romantic nonsense! Your blood was crying out for a man, and he was there and wanted you.'

'We loved each other!'

'Have it your own way. In any case, you weren't the iceberg then that you are now.' He thrust his head forward. 'Didn't your pulses quicken when he was close to you? Whether you call it love or sex instinct, it's a good thing sometimes to feel human desire running through you. You're a warm-blooded woman, you can't go on denying your emotions.'

Elena clasped her arms to stop herself from trembling. Such things were not spoken of — he had no right to mention them — and he knew far too much, to talk with such brutal accuracy of feelings she had made herself forget.

28

She weighed her words carefully. 'What are you doing, General Marint? Aren't you like a horrid little boy with an insect, poking it to see how it squirms? I am not squirming any more for you.'

She got to her feet and turned away, but he was up quickly and had caught her by the shoulder, pulling her round to face him.

'Is that what you think I'm doing? That I'm just amusing myself for half an hour, arousing you to no purpose? I wouldn't do anything so pointless!'

'I can't see any point in this.'

'I'm trying to make you realize that you've got to live like a woman, not a machine. God knows why *me* but someone's got to do it.' The fingers were pressing into her shoulder so tightly that it hurt. 'You can't push all your emotions into the grave with a dead man. Look at me. Admit it.'

'I don't admit it,' she answered stiffly, but against her will she stopped staring at his chin and looked up. She met the full gaze of his hazel eyes, searching her own deeply.

'Then I'll prove it.'

He released her shoulder and his arms slid around her. It was so quick that there was no evading him. She was held in hard, strong arms against his chest, and she felt his sheer masculinity sweep over her like a breaking wave.

He bent his head and pressed his mouth to hers. Her heart was pounding and the blood throbbed in her ears, and still he held her although she resisted, trying to push him away. The kiss was long and passionate and inescapable.

At last he raised his head. 'I was right. Your cheeks are pink and you're breathing quicker. You're still alive. I'll make a woman of you yet.'

Elena nearly choked with fury. Her hand lifted to smack his face, but some small streak of caution prevented her. It might precipitate too much. But she was too enraged to stay a moment longer in the same room with him. She flung her hair back and turned sharply to the door.

'I don't need remodelling by you – you high-handed

conceited brigand!'

He swept up her towel and handed it to her with a small bow. His smile was mocking her again.

'Good, Señorita Moural. You are thawing already. In future, off parade, you may call me Gregor — when you run out of other names.'

Feeling as if she had completely lost the last shreds of her dignity Elena fled upstairs, and Gregor Marint, still smiling, sat down to his supper.

CHAPTER THREE

The orderly had returned from Puenterojo; in the office General Marint was sitting at the desk sorting through the papers which had just been brought in.

'There's a letter for Señora Moural here,' he remarked.

Elena was working at the table near the window; as she got up he placed the envelope on the corner of the desk.

'Thank you. I'll give it to Carmela to take upstairs.'

As she walked down the corridor she looked at the envelope. Varena. And Uncle Pablo's hand. Her mother must have asked his advice about Valdoro; she always liked to hear the family opinions on important matters, though she rarely let them influence her own. So far the General had not told Doña Luisa what compensation she might expect, but however small somehow the house must be salvaged, Elena said grimly to herself.

She had not yet sounded out the possibility of a permanent office post; she had the uncomfortable feeling that after the incident with Marint on the night of the cattle drive (which she had mentioned to no one) it might be capable of misconstruction.

Thank heaven there had been no more such occurrences. Not by one word, not by so much as a glance had he recalled that evening. His behaviour to her was a model of decorum; when he handed papers to her their fingers never touched; never once when she had been working had he come and stood behind her, or leaned over her shoulder. He could not have been better behaved. Then why . . .?

She was ready to believe that he had acted on a sudden impulse, that all he intended was to shock her into a realization of what she was doing. And in that he had

31

succeeded. She hated to admit it, but he was right.

She *had* been burying her emotions in Vicente's grave, and it was not a good thing. It had been necessary at first to allow her wounds to heal a little, so that she could bear to go on living, but once she had reached the stage of acceptance it had been a mistake to dull her own sensitivities so deliberately. If she went on doing so, she would end as one of those dried-up spinsters who spend their lives doing Christian works in a singularly cold and un-Christian manner.

But if Marint had only meant to shock her he had gone much too far. It surely was not necessary to tell her that she was going to belong to him, and to kiss her. Such a remark could only be interpreted one way, she thought, and felt a hot flush rise to her face.

She was almost ready to hate him, but one couldn't quite hate a man who treated one as considerately as he did. He was thoughtful in small matters. He never smoked in the office if she was there, and by and large, he never stressed the *fait accompli* of the transference of ownership of Valdoro. He was not a boor, whatever her mother or Cristina might say. She remembered how he had gone with her to the stables and asked her permission to use her riding horses; he had caressed each one, and even Diablo stopped rolling his eyes and lowered his muzzle to be patted. That was surprising; even more so was the fact that old Pedro was quite happy that he should ride the big black stallion, if he wished.

'Ah, *Hija*!' he had said when they were alone, his leathery nut-brown face wrinkling into a delighted smile, 'Do not fear. He will handle Diablo well. Already they are friends. Yes, he is a man, and he knows horses, that one.'

From Pedro there was no higher praise.

Perhaps Marint knew women, too, and how to handle them. How many had he kissed as he had kissed her? Her cheeks flamed again. It had been shocking, and yet — and yet — it had been exciting to be in a man's arms again, to feel hard muscle, a rough cheek, a warm strong mouth. It was simply a physical reaction, sex instinct he had called it, and she was furious with herself since it was so unexpectedly beyond her control. He had been right even about that!

But speculation would not get her anywhere; she had far better forget the whole matter, and get on with the day's work.

'Carmela! There is a letter for the Señora!'

Elena, her blushes under control, returned to the office, and Carmela padded off with the letter.

The day wore on, and Doña Luisa said nothing of importance, made no reference to the letter. After dinner would be the best time to tell the girls, she had decided. It was annoying that the General would be joining them for the meal. Frequently he stayed so late on his outside inspections that Carmela had to give him a solitary supper, but on the rare occasions when he returned in time Doña Luisa was bound by courtesy to invite him to her table.

Tonight, it seemed, the General did not care whether he talked or not. Elena suspected he was secretly amused by her mother's thinly veiled animosity, Cristina's distaste and wariness, and her own attempts to balance tactfully between the two ends of the see-saw, knowing that any time he chose he could use his weight to overthrow the three of them.

But the balance had been maintained; Marint had refused a second cup of coffee and bidden them good night.

The three women were alone together in the drawing-room, with the scent of flowers flowing in upon them through the open windows leading to the patio. Outside the sky was a luminous violet blue; the courtyard would soon be in darkness and the stone pillars, the dark leaves of the shrubs, the peach tree and the blue Paraguayan jasmine would all melt and fuse together; so that until the moon rose the space between the house walls would be an area of mysterious obscurity, filled with vague shadows and blurred patches of paler gloom, thronged with the rustle of leaves, the sleepy twitter of birds, and the gentle splashing of the central fountain behind its almost invisible wrought-iron rails.

Doña Luisa settled herself against the sofa cushions and

looked from one girl to the other.

'Well, my dears, I have some news for you!'

She paused to make sure she had all their attention, and then went on. 'We are to have some guests. In three days' time. Don Felipe Castellan is coming to see me. I need his legal opinion about the sequestration, and I can't possibly go to Varena to get it. And someone else is coming with him. I'm sure you've guessed. Yes, Carlos! He has been so good and has offered to bring Don Felipe with him, so we shall have two visitors for a short while.'

'Why Carlos? And how long will they be staying, Mother?' asked Elena as calmly as she could. The news was totally unexpected.

'Only two or three days, I'm afraid, but it will be a lovely change for us, won't it? But that isn't all. My news is much more exciting than that. Why Carlos, indeed! Of course, your Uncle Pablo wants to know how we are getting on, but Carlos is coming for quite a different reason, too. I'll come straight out with it. He is proposing marriage again. You are a very lucky girl, Elena. Most young men would be far too proud to offer twice for the same girl. And in our present circumstances, just think how generous it is. You won't be taking with you the dowry you would have had five years ago. Nevertheless – '

'Mother!' Elena broke in sharply. 'Do you mean that you have accepted Carlos without even asking me?'

'Of course not, darling! I have told him he may come and make his first approaches to you, that's all. But surely there is only one possible answer? You are twenty-four, and eligible young men are very scarce. Besides, there are very few families who want a bride who comes to her husband empty-handed.'

'That sort of husband wouldn't be worth having,' Elena said very quietly.

'It might not be his decision, as you well know. And that is immaterial. In this case Don Pablo and Carlos are both perfectly happy. All they want is to join our two families again. It isn't likely that your birth alone will be enough

34

recommendation elsewhere, in this materialist society. Now with Cristina it will be much easier. She is younger, and she has her own money; she will have plenty of chances still. But *you* must make the most of this one.'

'I'm sorry, Mother. I won't do it.' Elena's face set into firm lines.

'What a silly girl you are! You haven't seen Carlos for three years! Just because you weren't ready for marriage five years ago you think nothing has altered! You have grown up; Carlos has had time to look around and make sure that he really wants you. That should be enough to endear him to you, I should think!'

'You should have asked me, Mother. You had no right to let him come. I don't want to marry him now any more than I did then.'

'Elena, for goodness sake try to act like a grown-up woman! How can you say how you will feel at this stage? I am not asking you to commit yourself, merely to entertain him on the understanding that marriage is being considered.

'Give yourself time. When you meet again you may feel quite differently. At nineteen you were very young for your age. You have had a wonderful offer; at least show that you have the sense and the courtesy to consider it. Now I have said my say; we will not talk about it any more this evening.'

So there is nothing more to be said at present, thought Elena, but her heart sank. This time she would be fighting her mother's wishes without her father's support. The immediate future, shadowed by her mother's hurt displeasure and cold disapproval, looked bleak.

It was unusual for Doña Luisa to ask to see Elena before she went riding; no doubt she had some special instructions as Carlos would be with them, Elena thought, as her mother presented her cheek to be kissed.

'Don Felipe is not riding, is he? Oh no, he said we would have a discussion on Valdoro while you young people were out, so I must get up and dress soon. I wanted to see you,

35

chiquita, about your riding clothes.'

'What about them, Mother?'

'Well, you are not going to wear your usual atrocious outfit, are you? Not in front of a guest!'

'Mother, you know perfectly well I haven't any other.'

Doña Luisa lifted her hands and let them fall back on to the quilt.

'Elena! You have a perfect outfit in the wardrobe! Your fiesta suit!'

Amazement and rebellious distaste swept Elena. 'My fiesta suit! I can't possibly wear that now! It was made for celebrations, when everybody is dressed up. It would look too pretentious altogether for a morning ride.'

Doña Luisa's voice lost its persuasion, and took on a note of authority.

'Elena, I cannot have you seen by guests in that dirty, dilapidated outfit. It would be an absolute insult to Carlos to go out riding with him in those clothes. So do as I say.'

'I can't, Mother. It will look as if I'm showing off, dressing up for Carlos's approval.'

'And why not? You shouldn't be ashamed of trying to appear at your best! It's the least a girl can do for a man who has done her the honour of asking if he may pay his addresses. Whatever your private feelings are, I will not allow you to be so discourteous as to expect him to escort a girl who looks like a down-at-heel horsebreaker.'

Elena knew she was beaten. If she was going to win her fight and refuse Carlos she could not afford to let her mother accuse her of being unco-operative, of deliberately putting him off.

'Very well. I'll go and change.'

Perhaps she deserved it, Elena thought. The suit had been the outcome of her caprice in the first place.

Before the war, at fiesta time, it had been the custom of the Mourales to join in the processions which played such a big part in the celebrations. Everyone who was anyone went to the fiesta in Varena; all the *estancieros* in the province vied

36

with each other in showing their finest horses, and the riders dressed up in elaborate traditional clothes for the occasion. The girls in their Spanish-style, many-flounced dresses would ride pillion behind their *novios* or, if not promised in marriage, with a disengaged man of their family.

One year Elena had rebelled; she was too old to ride pillion with her father, she did not wish to ride with her brother. She did not say so, but she knew Cristina wanted to ride with him. Elena insisted she wanted to be independent: besides, she rode as well as the men.

Her father was amused. 'Well, *querida*, what will you do? You cannot ride by yourself as a girl, and as I am not a magician I cannot turn you into a boy for the day.'

Then he laughed outright. 'But yes, I think I can! I have a splendid idea.'

And so, despite Doña Luisa's protests, Elena was taken to the tailor and a suit was made for her, a replica of the ones worn by the Riquezan dandies, a magnificent suit.

The slim black trousers had silver decoration down the side seams, and the jacket, close-fitting and cropped short at the waist, had the same decoration on collar and fronts which were linked across with silver chains to clasps fashioned like pumas' heads. The brief jacket showed a white silk shirt and a broad belt of pale fawn leather, also ornamented in a pattern of silver studs set with topazes. There were gloves to match the belt, and the outfit was completed with shiny black riding boots and a black sombrero with a silver-fringed brim.

And this outfit, which Doña Luisa had disapproved of her wearing at the fiesta, saying it was too revealing, she now insisted on her putting on for a morning ride with Carlos.

Elena hoped it wouldn't fit. But it did, perfectly.

Up to the moment when Carlos de Zurga saw Elena in the fiesta suit he was completely neutral about her. At dinner the previous evening she had struck him as being detached. disinterested to the point of coldness. Carlos liked women who were aware of their own physical attractions, and of his, and

37

who showed it in secret glances and sly little smiles, in all the alphabet of coquetry. If they were prepared to take the matter further, so much the better, though with single girls of good family it was of course impossible. It would be very bad form, and much too risky.

But the married women of his acquaintance had no scruples about deceiving their husbands, who were probably busy conducting their own extra-marital *affaires*, and he did not find it difficult to reach terms of intimacy with almost any one of them when he chose. By managing such associations with great expertise he obtained pleasure with variety.

He did not expect marriage to provide him with enjoyment of the same degree of piquancy, but in view of the arrangements made with his father Elena would be perfectly satisfactory.

She was certainly beautiful; but viewing her dispassionately across the dinner table he had decided she had not enough style. Her simple dinner dress was not smart enough for his tastes, it gave her no distinction, and her manner to him was completely lacking in coquetry, even of interest. She would be adequate, no more.

But when Elena walked into the stable court in her fiesta suit Carlos could not take his eyes off her.

In the brilliant sunshine her black-clad figure stood out sharply, the lines of her body stressed by the close-fitting suit. She was slim, beautifully boned, deliciously curved.

She mounted her horse in one glorious continuous movement, gripping the animal expertly between sharp, shapely legs. Her vitality was electrifying. All at once she was a different woman, not the girl he thought he had known for years. She vibrated with energy, she was a creature of stunning physical attraction. This, he decided, would be a conquest worth making. He had been going about this matter in quite the wrong way; by holding back he had probably caused her indifference. He would now court her. And so he began paying her little compliments, at the same time letting his eyes admire her more than his words did. He gave her quite unnecessary assistance, he paid unusual attention to her views on any and every subject of conversation, he sat where he could see her and serve her.

So I'm getting the full treatment, Elena thought cynically, as she dressed for dinner. He's being a good boy and doing his best to please, as no doubt his father has ordered him. All this fuss to impress her now — it would be very short-lived after the wedding ceremony. She would be little more than a chattel then. He didn't attract her, and he needn't think he was deceiving her. He might behave as he pleased, she wouldn't raise any objections — but she wouldn't marry him.

She dismissed him and thought instead of Gregor Marint who was to have dinner with them that night — he had not yet met their guests. Three more divergent male types could hardly be imagined. Don Felipe was middle-aged, short and stout, with a quick dry wit which Elena enjoyed as much as she admired his broadmindedness, and moderate views, qualities which the majority of men in their society did not possess. He was extremely well-read, with a legal incisiveness of mind, but he also appreciated the more worldly pleasures of food and drink, and was a wide-ranging and entertaining conversationalist. Carlos lacked Don Felipe's breadth of mind as much as his physical girth. He was more restricted by the conventions of their class, although he was well-travelled and liked to pretend to cosmopolitan behaviour and mental attitudes. But really it hadn't got much beyond a habit of smoking North American cigarettes — on strict import licence — instead of their own Riquezan brands.

Marint would be very much the odd man out. He would know the other men would be in evening dress, but it was extremely unlikely that he would have anything as formal as a dinner jacket. In his casual clothes he would look impossibly uncultivated — but then he might not care, he might even prefer to look like a peasants' leader.

If, on the other hand, he wanted to be formal, he might wear his dress uniform. That, although strictly correct, would not only look pretentious but would be in very bad taste for a

39

private dinner so soon after the end of the war in which he had been on the winning side and the rest of the party the losers. His behaviour was as unpredictable as his costume; she gave up her speculations, finished dressing, and left her room to go downstairs.

Doña Luisa glanced at the clock for the third time. In four minutes she would have to decide whether to wait for the General or to start without him. She could not very well do the latter, she supposed; if he had no courtesy she must still retain hers.

Then there was the sound of crisp footsteps on the staircase. Elena heard them, but Carlos was talking to her, doing his best to hold her attention, so from politeness she did not look up until the General reached them. She was just in time to see him approach Doña Luisa and give her a brief but polished bow. His remark was quiet, but perfectly audible to them all.

'My apologies, Señora Moural. I have no evening dress with me.'

Doña Luisa, by a great effort, managed not to show surprise; Elena, as all eyes were on Marint, was saved the trouble.

As she had expected, he was perfectly groomed, but she had not dreamed that he would have the subtlety to turn his lack of evening dress to a positive advantage. His appearance put the other two men in the shade, and gave a touch of irony to his smooth apology.

He was wearing trousers of black linen, tapered and beautifully cut, with a fine white shirt which was absolutely plain, and finished with a very narrow black tie. Around his waist was wound the sash which Riquezan men wear at fiesta time; of bright scarlet, one fringed end hanging at the left side, it joined with the black trousers in accentuating the leanness of waist and hips. All this was topped with a linen jacket, which sat with faultless style and emphasized with its smooth whiteness the magnificent shoulders which Elena for one, having seen him in shirt-sleeves, knew owed nothing to the tailor.

She saw her mother greet him quite graciously and turn to introduce the other two men.

He bowed courteously to them both, and at that moment dinner was announced. Doña Luisa put her arm in Don Felipe's, and they began to move away. Without apparent haste Gregor Marint was at Elena's side before Carlos had collected his wits. He offered her his arm; the look in his eyes and the faint smile on his lips were a challenge.

She rose and put her hand on his sleeve, leaving Carlos to bring up the rear with Cristina. Elena could not help feeling a sly pleasure that Carlos was outwitted by a perfectly legitimate move; she was not engaged to Carlos, Marint had every right to claim precedence.

The dinner went astonishingly well. Gregor Marint showed them a side of himself at which none of them had guessed. His brusque and downright manner had vanished; he was urbane, polished, ready to talk on any subject from horses and cars to measures for improving the national economy and the peasants' living conditions.

He did not attempt to dominate a discussion, but he would listen and then make some remark which showed he had seen straight to the heart of a problem. For some time now Elena had been fairly sure of the qualities which had enabled him to become a General; now she saw more clearly why he had been made a Minister.

He was matching them on their own ground, showing them that one did not have to be born of their blue blood to be able to behave and converse in a civilized and cultivated manner.

The rest of the party was taken aback, each trying to conceal their own reactions, but Elena, knowing them well could guess at them all. Señor Castellán was not involved, and he was pleased to find the General such agreeable company. Doña Luisa was amazed and suspicious: surely he had some hidden motive in being so pleasant? Carlos was irritated; he would resent not being able to feel superior to Marint. As for Cristina, she was resentful too, and as suspicious as her godmother.

After dinner Marint made his excuses, leaving the other men to smoke their cigars. Carlos took the opportunity of having a private talk with Don Felipe, but this was brief, and they soon joined the ladies in the small drawing-room which they now used in preference to the large salon.

CHAPTER FOUR

Everyone agreed it had been a most delightful three days.

Privately there were certain reservations. First, although he had enjoyed the luxury of indolence Don Felipe thought he could scarcely afford it at this time. Doña Luisa had brought him out here prematurely. He did not need to come out to Valdoro to get her agreement to Don Pablo's settlement proposals; until she had Elena's consent there was nothing for him to do here. He would go back to Varena and get the documents drawn up, since Doña Luisa had told him they must be ready.

Carlos considered he might have been given more opportunity to be alone with Elena; one could be too conventional, and if the rules had been waived a little he might have made more headway. But next time, he promised himself, it would be different.

The black and chrome Thunderbird was waiting outside the main door, and the men were making their formal goodbyes. Carlos came up to Elena and gave her a cousinly kiss on both cheeks, as convention allowed, then took her hand and raised it to his lips, a gesture usually reserved in Riqueza as a mark of respect to married women or a greeting of lovers. But why? thought Elena. Surely Mother has told him?

She remembered uncomfortably the scene with her mother the previous evening. She had been getting ready for bed when Doña Luisa had knocked on her door, and had sat down to talk with her.

'It can't be left until tomorrow morning, there will be no time then, and I must know what I am to say to Carlos.'

Elena stopped brushing her hair and looked at her mother.

'I'm sorry, Mother, but I still don't want to marry him.'

43

Doña Luisa sat and stared at her, her lips pressed together, trying not to answer hastily.

'Elena, it is time you looked at this matter rationally. I understand that Carlos may not be exactly your ideal of a husband, but if you refuse him you must consider the alternatives.'

'I have, Mother, and I prefer them.'

The cool answer fanned Doña Luisa's suppressed wrath.

'Then I wonder what you consider them to be? Do you think that, if you wait, a second Vicente Vargas will come out of the blue to marry you?'

It was a cruel thing to say, but the girl had to be shaken up. Elena said nothing.

'I'm sorry, Elena, but I can't have you spoiling your life because of him. He's dead, and it's no use looking for someone else like him.'

'That part of my life is over and done with. I'm not looking for someone like him, that would be foolish. I just don't fancy Carlos as a husband, that's all.'

'Then who do you think you are going to get if you refuse him? You surely don't want to stay single, do you? Our life is going to be different from now on. I haven't talked about it because I don't want you to think it worries me, but you must know that I am going to have very little money. If we stay here, there will be none of the old-style entertaining, no town house and no seaside villa as there used to be, and therefore no opportunity to make new friends. And if we leave here and go to live in Varena we shall still have to live very quietly – "

'We can't leave here, Mother!' Elena interrupted vehemently.

'You surely don't want to stay under the present conditions? We shall positively moulder away, confined here with nothing to do and nowhere to go. It was bad enough while the war was on, but at least we were away from the fighting and there was the estate to care for – '

'Mother, you can't sell Valdoro!'

'May I remind you that I have been robbed of most of it

44

already? The house may as well go with the rest of it.'

'*No*!'

'I am beginning to think you are a complete sentimentalist! First you cling to your memories of young Vargas, now you're clinging to this house. It's not rational! If you marry you will be able to start a new life, in a new place, with new interests, new society — everything will open up for you again, you will be able to enjoy life. And with an establishment of your own, a husband and children, you won't have time to grieve over Valdoro.'

'I dare say you're right, Mother — ' Elena was trying to be patient — 'but I don't want Carlos as a husband. I know you will be short of money, but there's nothing to prevent me from earning my living until I find a man I want to marry.'

Doña Luisa was aghast. 'Earn your living! What do you think you are? The daughter of a tradesman? How can you suggest such a thing!'

'There's nothing wrong with taking a job; in fact I think it's more honest than marrying a man to share his money and position.'

'Honest! What fiddlesticks! Marriage is a woman's job. There's nothing dishonest about choosing a man who can maintain you properly! You are not deceiving me, Elena, you have some romantic ideal and you're waiting to meet someone who fills it. But I can tell you this — you won't! I will tell you what your alternative will be if you refuse Carlos. There are no eligible young men left in our society who will marry a landless, penniless girl of twenty-four. There are only the ones who are so unattractive that no one will take them. I dare say if I look around I can find you some repulsive cripple, or a decadent half-wit who will be eager to marry you, simply to have a wife! Is that the sort of husband you want?'

'Mother, do you have to be so revoltingly sordid?'

'Yes. I have to make you see sense. Here you have a spendid offer, from a young man who is very much in love with you. Oh, I know he may have been a little — gay — but he will settle down with you, because he wants you. And he will know how

45

to give you pleasure. When you give him children — '

'No, Mother! The very thought of it — not with Carlos! I don't love him — I don't even like him. If you go on like this I shall hate him. I won't marry him. I tell you I'll stay single · '

Doña Luisa rose to her feet. 'I can see it is useless to talk to you now. You are becoming hysterical. I am almost beginning to wonder if these last few years have not made you a trifle - unnatural. But I insist that you think over what I have said, and face the facts calmly. I will let the matter rest. But I am not going to send Carlos away with a refusal; I shall ask for a little more time for you to consider. If you have a grain of sense you will realize what is to your advantage, before it is too late to accept him.'

She left without saying good night, leaving Elena in a very low-spirited state of mind.

It was horrible that her own mother should talk to her like that. But she could not believe that there was no alternative to marrying Carlos or taking some even more repulsive husband. If she had a permanent salaried post at Valdoro, surely her mother would not consider leaving, and would shelve the question of marriage?

Gregor Marint was in the office, sitting at the desk thumbing through some papers when Elena went in.

'General Marint, may I ask you something?'

'Of course. Sit down.'

As she did so she decided that with such a man it was pointless to beat about the bush.

'I want to know whether I may have a permanent post in the office here,' she said without preamble.

It was a moment before he spoke. 'But, Señorita Moural, I thought you understood that this position was only temporary, that there was no question of it being a permanency?'

'In a way, yes. But I'm not asking for the post of estate manager, I'm only asking for an office job. You've been satisfied with my work, I think?'

'You are most efficient. But I must have a man here,

46

responsible for all the outside work as well. Under my system you couldn't do that.'

'I'm not asking to do that. But if I did the bulk of the office work it would leave the manager more free for outside supervision, wouldn't it?'

She paused, but Marint said nothing. Apprehension was rising in her; she hurried on. 'If you don't think there's enough clerical work to keep me busy full time, I should be prepared to do it as a part-time job for a reduced salary.'

Desperation was beginning to clutch at Elena's throat. He was showing no sign of agreement -- but he must not refuse. It was vital to her.

'Señorita Moural, I am a State employee just as you are. I cannot put in two people where I know one will do. It's uneconomical. Oh, I can understand that you have personal reasons for wanting to stay here, but you must realize that it wouldn't work. Your position as a humble office employee would be quite different from that of *La Hija de Valdoro*.' He gave her a little smile. 'Even if no one else rubbed it in, you'd feel it.'

Her mouth set obstinately. 'I should learn to put up with it. I don't want to leave here, and I *do* want to earn my own living.'

'You want to earn your own living?' His eyebrows lifted a little. 'Now that's praiseworthy, from one of your upbringing. The country needs every educated woman who is willing to work -- there won't be enough for some years to come. Does you mother know about this?'

His look was shrewd and ironic. I mustn't let him make me angry, she thought. And I won't answer.

'Well, does she?'

'I didn't tell her I was asking you for this job.'

'No. And I dare say she has other plans. What if she gives up this house?'

'I could still work here.' Elena answered doggedly, knowing the impossibility of it.

'Come now, Señorita Moural, that is pure fantasy! Let me

47

give you a little advice.'

'I suppose I can't stop you,' she answered bitterly.

'That's no way to speak to an employer,' he remarked drily. 'You're not in practice yet, are you? This is what I was going to say. I am in no hurry for you to finish here, so why not bide your time until you know Señora Moural's plans? If she decides to leave here there would be plenty of jobs you could do wherever you go.

'If you're in Varena — well, there are vacant posts in my Ministry, for a start. If you have any difficulty in getting a job I will provide you with a reference on the basis of your work here.' He gave her a grin. 'That might cause a little gossip but it would get you a post, of that I'm certain.'

Gossip! That she could imagine . . .

'Thank you very much,' she said stiffly. 'I hope that will not be necessary. I'll think about what you have said.'

She stood up.

'I'm sorry I can't do it,' he said.

She nodded, went to her own table, and started work.

It was very difficult to concentrate on her papers when her own affairs seemed so much more immediate and important. If she hadn't a paying post here, she would be completely in her mother's hands, and would have to go wherever her mother went, for she hadn't a *peso* of ready money — except for what she had just earned — apart from such allowances as Doña Luisa saw fit to give her. It was humiliating that, at twenty-four, she still had to have her mother's signature before she could touch a single coin of the settlement her father had made her.

She could still refuse to marry Carlos and try to find a post wherever her mother decided to live, but she could imagine the reaction that would provoke. The atmosphere would be practically unbearable, and her mother was not above attempting by subtle coercion to get her own way. She could certainly make every conceivable difficulty.

In a moment of weakness Elena even wondered whether she had not better start looking for Carlos's good points after all.

to see whether she could possibly adapt herself to the thought of marriage with him. She would at least have access to her own money on her marriage – though it wasn't much for her father had always intended her to have a handsome marriage settlement, and according to her mother, that was now impossible.

No, not Carlos, please, not Carlos, she was almost praying, when she realized that Marint was speaking to her.

'Señorita Moural, I thought that no one could embarrass me, but I believe you've given me a unique experience. I am actually choosing my words for my next speech to you.'

She looked across at him in surprise.

'I had intended to ask you a favour this morning. I am sure you won't feel co-operative, and I'm sorry there's nothing I can do to ease it. I can't alter my plans. But they are not directed against you personally, believe me.'

'Plans?' Her heart began to sink; what else was there to come?

'Let me explain my position. You know I have the job of taking over the large *estancias* and turning them into State Farms. Most of them in the past have been run by their owners, with foremen responsible to them, working foremen, who knew nothing of the business side. With the owners gone, I need capable farm managers – and I want more than that. I want men who can be mobile, who can manage any farm, and co-ordinate their policies under me, and have other capabilities which I shall need, but won't bother you with.

'I have some men in mind, but most of them need up-to-date experience – a bit of post-war practice and polish you might say. This I intend to give them, by leaving them in charge for a spell on an estate – preferably a well-run one, for a start. Valdoro is one place I think will make an excellent training ground. It's a compliment to you that I find this place in such good order.'

'You pay me some very odd compliments, General Marint.'

'Do I? You're lucky to get any at all from me. I don't mix business and pleasure. As I was saying, Valdoro is well-run, and

49

as I shan't be here much longer I intend to get one of my men out here as soon as possible to get the feel of the place before I leave. He will do a spell here, bring in another man, put him wise to things, and move on.

'It would be a great help to me if you were prepared to give my man the benefit of your knowledge. But please don't think you would be training your successor. No one will succeed you. Anyone who comes here will simply be a State employee. But it would be a good thing if we could all work together — after all, it's up to each of us to try to make Riqueza a good land for everyone to live in — it's the only way to make the last few years worth while.'

I believe he really means it, she thought. His own aggrandizement isn't the important thing. He really wants to improve conditions, and this is his way of making a start. But what utter effrontery! Of course I shall be training my successor — how else could it be, when these men of his are going to take over as managers? It's sheer sophistry, and the fact that he has convinced himself doesn't alter the case.

But it was beneath her to argue about it, just as it would be beneath her to vent her sense of personal injury on the trainee manager.

'I'll do what I can to help him when he comes.' She swallowed the lump in her throat which the fresh hurt had brought, and tried to look as if she didn't care. 'You'll want accommodation for him, of course?'

'If you please. These lads are not bunk-house boys, you'll find them quite house-trained.'

He grinned at her. She could almost hear him thinking: I know where your mother would have sent me if she'd had the chance.

His teeth shone whitely, his eyes were crinkling at the corners, and that cleft had appeared in his cheek; he was attractive, and it irritated her. Attractive? He was like a strong, healthy animal, that was all. No, it wasn't all. He had a brain, he had ideas, but he was an extremist, he wanted to bring everyone down to the same level. Or up? Perhaps he'd like to

50

fill Valdoro House with *peones* and plantation women?

Well, she'd arrange to accommodate his manager -- and she wouldn't forget to claim for his board and lodging, either.

Two days later the manager arrived.

Marint saw Elena in the corridor as he came from the stables. 'My sergeant has just got back with the new man. Will you come along and meet him?' he asked.

They went to the office; Marint opened the door and stood aside for her to enter.

A man was standing in front of the window with his back to them. A young man, tall and slim; the sunlight was giving him a cap of gold. It was a trick, he couldn't have such fair hair -- there was only one man who had hair like that! Now he was turning round and the floor was rising up, everything was rocking and dissolving into a blur of colour. Her hand clutched the edge of the desk, for her legs had turned into rubber and she couldn't see anything properly. Through the surging roar in her ears she heard Marint's voice.

'Señorita Moural, this is -- '

The room was steadying, and a face swam into view before her eyes -- a face she knew -- a face that was concerned, and questioning, with lips that moved and made sounds, sounds that became words, words which said, 'Señorita Moural and I are already acquainted. I used to know her brother.'

It was older, that face, and thinner. It had strange lines, and eyes that held more pain, a mouth that had tasted bitterness. Of course it had -- it had been stopped with gravedust two years ago, when Vicente died. But this man -- this man was alive -- and he was indeed Vicente.

Standing behind her Marint had apparently been unaware that, for the space of three or four seconds, Elena had nearly fainted, had recovered by sheer willpower, and had forced herself to speak with a pretence of lightness and normality.

'I didn't expect to see someone I know. It's quite a shock, after so long.'

'So you know each other!' Marint had remarked. 'In that

51

case I'll leave you to have a gossip before you settle down to work.'

And with that he had gone.

'I'm sorry, Elena,' Vicente said 'I tried not to come.'

Elena moved round behind the desk and sat down. She had a feeling of unreality, as if this were happening to some other person.

What on earth did Vicente mean by 'I tried not to come'? He, too, seemed like another person, not pleased to see her at all, only confused and embarrassed. It *was* Vicente, with his astonishingly fair hair and grey-blue eyes – so odd in a Riquezan, and so attractive – yet a Vicente two years older, ill at ease, not behaving like a man who loved her.

'Why didn't you tell me? How could you let me go on thinking you were dead?'

It was not the way she should have greeted him. In the early days after the report of his death, before she had realized that for her own good she must face what she thought to be the truth, she had fancied that he might still be alive, and even had imagined their reunion. She, between laughing and crying, would be caught in his arms, held and kissed, spoken to with love, held and kissed again. They would be lost in the wonder of finding each other.

She had not thought of anything like this. It was all so wrong; nothing was as it should be.

'I did it for the best. You shouldn't have known. I never intended it.'

'For the best! Don't you understand – I could have borne anything if I'd just known you were alive! Nothing could be as bad as death.'

She put out a hand, but he did not take it.

'You don't know. It would have been better the other way. All this – it's just an opening of old wounds. It's agony for both of us.'

She felt even more confused. 'Why should it be, Vicente? I just can't understand why you let me go on thinking you were dead.'

52

He sat down, not beside her but round the corner of the desk.

'You've had one shock today. Can you take some more? Because if I've got to explain, I may as well do it now, and then we can start afresh. But it's going to upset you.'

'I must know your reason. Whatever it is, I can stand it now I know you're alive.'

'Are you sure you want to know?' he insisted.

'Yes, I'm sure.'

Oh, please God, whatever the mystery, let us have it out in the open!

'Very well. Then I'll have to start from the beginning. I'll have to tell you a story.'

He would not look at her, but stared down at his hands clenched together on the desk top.

'Once upon a time there was a man, an *estanciero*. He was rich, his ranch was nearly as big as Valdoro. He was married, he had children. But a young servant girl took his fancy. He seduced her, he visited her frequently, and some time later she found she was pregnant.'

His face was expressionless, he was struggling to keep all emotion out of his voice. It sounded hard and flat. Elena began to feel a dreadful sinking sensation within her, her eyes were fixed on his face.

'He treated her very well by his standards. He found her a husband and set them both up in a little shop in Varena, where no one would know anything about the affair. A few months later I was born.'

Suddenly the bitterness he had been holding back flooded out, and his voice sharpened.

'Yes, that's the beginning of my story. Rather squalid, isn't it?' He paused, and then resumed more calmly. 'Oh, don't think I had a hard life — rather the reverse. My stepfather is a good man; he had always been fond of my mother, and he has loved me like his own sons. My mother grew to love him.

'A polite fiction was established that I had a rich godfather. That explained why I went to an expensive school, and my younger brothers and sisters did not, why later on I went to the university, while they helped with the business. Eventually, of course, I guessed the truth. I saw my father once, in a lawyer's office, before I started at the university. I knew he was my father, and he knew, but nothing was acknowledged. All I had to do was to say, "Yes, sir," and "No, sir," at the right moments.'

'Oh, Vicente, how awful for you,' Elena whispered.

'You think you understand, but you can't know what it did to me. And then at university — the other fellows used talk about their fathers' *estancias*, their horses and so forth — can you imagine how often I wanted to shout, "My father has a ranch twice the size of yours, you braggart. I'm as well-born as you are!" But instead I had to put up with sly remarks about Vargas's little shop. Why, even my name should have been different! The decent men like your brother never mentioned my background. And then I met you.'

Elena held her breath.

'I was in love with you before I realized what was happening. And when I found you were in love with me, it was all so wonderful I didn't think about the consequences at first. When I did face them, I saw how impossible it was. Your parents would never consider your marrying a shopkeeper's son. And it wouldn't have made matters any better if I'd gone to your father and said, "My father's family is as good as yours, as noble, as wealthy, as blue-blooded. The only thing is, I was born on the wrong side of the blanket." As if they would have let you marry a bastard! Do you begin to understand what it was like for me?'

Elena nodded, unable to speak.

'There wasn't any solution, and it didn't get any better. Then the Revolution broke out, and at last there was something I could do. I joined up. You never enquired which side I was fighting on, did you? You just assumed I was with Luis, in the Volunteers. But do you think I was going to fight to keep a system which gave all the wealth and power into a few hands, so that a man like my father could seduce my

54

mother and escape all the consequences, all the responsibilities, merely by dipping into his bottomless pocket? I joined the Revolutionary Army.'

Oh, how much more? Elena cried to herself. If I had only known before. Now he is beyond my comfort.

'That isn't quite all,' he went on, as if he had read her thoughts. 'I was in a small engagement – just a skirmish really, with some Volunteers, and they got the worst of it. When they were well on the run we went to see what casualties they had sustained.'

He put his hand to his eyes, as if trying to wipe out the memory of it.

'They had taken their wounded, and left their dead. I came round some rocks, and found Luis. He was dead, of course – there was nothing I could do for him. But I did what I could do for you. I arranged for that farmer to keep his body with reverence until you could send for it. And I sent a message to Valdoro.'

The tears were running down Elena's cheeks, unchecked.

'So it was you,' she whispered.

'Just after that I was wounded myself, and when I heard I'd been reported dead I decided it was the best thing that could have happened. There never could have been a future for us, and for all I know I may even have killed your brother. The thought of that has haunted me ever since.'

She shook her head, struggling desperately to regain some composure.

'No, Vicente! You must never think that. I never shall. It's all over. It's only the future that concerns us now.'

Surely he could see that everything was different now? They were all at peace, and everything was changing, the old class systems were going with the break-up of the *estancias*, the past with all its hatred and bitterness must be forgotten. Her heart ached for him and for all he had suffered.

Without conscious thought ideas were forming in her mind. Now everything was different. If they still loved each other no one could prevent their marriage. They could have their happiness. She would stay with him, go wherever he went, and sometimes, even, they would stay together at Valdoro. Please God, let this be my solution! she prayed. Surely we still love each other enough?

Now for the first time he looked her full in the eyes.

'Now you really know me, Elena. You know how bitter I am, how resentful. You know how ashamed I am, and how guilty, too, for the way I've kept you in ignorance. But how could I face you?'

'Didn't you trust my love enough for that?'

'I don't know. It was the sheer perversity — the imposs-ibility of it ever coming right. Now at last I've told you. Please keep my secret. It's not a story I want known.'

'I shall never tell anyone.'

'Thank you, Elena. The fewer people know about it, the easier I feel. Though there are times when I can't stand the thought of it, I still have to live with it. About my birth, I've only told one person, and it was right that I should do that.'

'Why? Who was it?' she asked.

He answered her quite simply. 'I had to tell my wife.'

She had left Vicente as soon as she decently could, still hiding her shock and anguish, left him without even the touch of hands. The fact that she understood what had happened, and why, did not make her suffering any the less.

Vicente had given her up, because it seemed the only way. He had done so thinking it was the best for her to believe he was dead and to remake her life without him. If he had only waited! But he had found a second love, not the mad consuming adoration he had had for her, but something quieter, steadier, yet he had made it plain, no less beautiful. And he was happy. Thank God he was happy, or rather, he was as happy as he allowed himself to be with the past which had become such a nerve-stretching part of him. There was nothing she could do for him: that was the right of someone else.

She had gone upstairs to her bedroom, feeling that just this once she must release her emotions in a storm of tears.

At last the first fierce anguish spent itself, and she was conscious of resentment and bitterness that Fate should play such a shabby trick on her. Everything was conspiring against her; she was getting no help from any quarter, the situation was more than she could bear. Yet she would have to bear it. There was no escape that she could see.

CHAPTER FIVE

Elena settled herself thankfully into the corner of the railway carriage. The porter had stowed her cases away, and now she was alone, her compartment a little untroubled island in the midst of the station's hubbub. She was travelling first class, and it was unlikely that anyone would invade her privacy at Puenterojo.

This was something quite new to Elena, for she had never before travelled by train in Riqueza. For long journeys the family had always used the Rolls which, when she had gone to finishing school in Brazil, had delivered her to Varena Airport. Puenterojo Station was a new world to her. The first class carriage seemed uncomfortable, so what was third class travel like, on hard wooden seats, packed in with too many other people, some of them none too clean, and burdened with cheeses and hens?

There was a series of warning whistles, an irregular fusillade of slamming doors, then, with a prolonged and piercing shriek. the engine hissed, puffed, grunted, and slowly drew away.

Elena turned away from the window and opened the book she had brought with her. She must try to put Valdoro behind her for the time being. When she came back she would tackle her problems; just now a break was what she needed.

On her lap the book lay unregarded. It had been too much of a strain, having Vicente in the house, knowing what she now knew, and forcing herself to accept the fact that, although he was alive, he was no longer any part of her life. She was still too confused and hurt to know what she really felt about him. But love for him was out of the question. That was a part of her life which was ended, and when her emotions settled, friendship and affection were the most she could allow herself to feel.

Her mother, with patrician insolence not bothering to disguise her dislike for Vicente, had made no bones about her relief on hearing that he was married. At least he could now be no emotional obstacle in the way of Elena's marriage to Carlos; she had enough of the Moural pride, and he had shown the faithlessness to be expected of someone of low birth.

Elena knew that her mother was determined the de Zurga match should be carried through, and she was equally determined that it should not. But pressures were subtly being brought to bear, she was being subjected to a kind of emotional blackmail.

Her mother had her best interests at heart, she didn't want Elena to have to live a poverty-stricken existence. Carlos would take good care of her. Without a husband what would happen to her when Doña Luisa was gone? The fact that Doña Luisa was not yet fifty and in robust health made this consideration appear academic; but from Doña Luisa's attitude one would have thought she was tottering on the edge of the grave.

It was Marint who had made it easy for her to get away.

She had looked up from her ledger one morning to find his eyes upon her.

'Am I working you too hard?' he asked abruptly.

'No,' she replied, surprised. 'I am working as I am used to.'

'Then what is it? The hot summer, perhaps? For the last couple of weeks you've been looking — well, rather 'peaky'. Why?'

'I don't know. It's nothing.'

'When did you last have a holiday? Not just an odd day. When did you last get away from here for a decent spell?'

'I don't really remember. A year or so ago, I suppose.'

'You're fibbing. It was longer. Still, I won't argue with you. But it's time you had a break. Is there anywhere you can go at short notice — to a relative, perhaps?'

'I have an aunt in Varena.'

'Varena would be fine. The change to town life would be

stimulating.' He smiled across at her. 'Your aunt — is she an old tartar, or would she spoil you?'

'She's a darling. She always spoils me.'

'Then you ought to go there. You can have two weeks off — three if you like — Vargas is quite capable of managing on his own.'

What a man he was! As she had said the first day they met, like one of his own tanks. He had flattened her obstacles; she could certainly go if her mother agreed. It was odd, for in the last few weeks she had been longing to see and talk with Aunt Ana again.

'Please don't think I'm trying to push you out. You can come back here and work until your affairs are settled. But you need a holiday.'

She smiled at him. 'I don't always impute the worst motives to you, General Marint. Thank you, I'll see what can be arranged.'

It had been astonishingly easy, for her mother had readily agreed. Elena did not quite know why. Carlos had said that Varena was becoming gay again; perhaps her mother thought that a taste of town life would make her want more, would whet her appetite, for Valdoro had been an austere diet of late. Perhaps she also thought it would do Elena no harm to be out of Vicente's way.

As Marint himself was leaving Valdoro very soon, Vicente would be in sole charge - a hard touch of irony which her mother would find particularly galling.

Doña Luisa had wanted her to wait until Carlos could spend a night or two at Valdoro, so that she could drive back to Varena with him, but that was not Elena's plan. She wanted to go as soon as possible, so she would go by train.

Marint had been most helpful; he had instructed his orderly to drive her into Puenterojo in the jeep. She did not know if the orderly had been given any other directions, but the fact remained that he had commandeered a porter, helped her to get her ticket, found an empty carriage, and even handed her into it.

For all this Elena was very grateful, as she was ridiculously ignorant of the procedure on railway stations. Money had smoothed her path for so much of her life, and she was only just beginning to realize what it would mean to be without it.

The journey was long and tedious, for there were so many stops, each one prolonged by loading and unloading. The compartment gradually filled, but Elena ignored her travelling companions as much as possible and continued to be buried in her thoughts.

She had probably seen the last of Marint. By the time she returned to Valdoro he would have gone. She ought to consider that a good thing. He was a disturbing person, he made her question so many of the ideas and conventions she had been brought up to respect. She was prepared to move with the times, but at a steady pace; with Marint it was like travelling on an express train — and on the buffers, not in a compartment!

Progress was the important thing, not the comfort of a minority. Her family and others like it had to lose their lands and incomes and make what shift they could to live under harder conditions, so that the State could use their money and territories for the common good.

She had to admit that the majority of Riquezans were living in discomfort, more or less acute, some were even starving; but everything would depend on whether the rest of the Government had Marint's public spirit. If they had, there was a chance that the conditions of the poor might be improved by the use of the confiscated assets of the rich.

Why was she bothering about attitudes of mind? The truth was she found him disturbing in other ways.

His strength, his forcefulness, both mental and physical — they were all part of his attraction. The thought gave her a small shock. She had not realized until then that she actually found him attractive. Then it was just as well that she'd seen the last of him. She could not afford to be distracted by such an impossible man when she had her life to remake.

At last she had reduced her problems to two First, how to

get rid of the de Zurga marriage proposal, and second, how to insist on her independence. Saying no – no – no – wasn't as easy as it sounded.

It might be best to start with her independence. If she could get a reasonably well-paid post she could tell her mother that she could support herself, and felt entitled to stand out for her personal rights even to the extent of refusing a marriage on which her mother had set her heart. Yes, a job would be a strong weapon, and while she was in Varena she must make some opportunity to look for one.

A stir in the carriage brought her back to reality. People were collecting up their papers, getting their luggage down from racks, making ready to leave the train the moment it reached the platform. They were nearly in Varena. One of the men in her carriage helped her with her cases, and after a few bewildering moments of indecision a porter saw her standing by the train and came forward. She followed him through the barrier and he hailed a taxi for her.

'Avenida de Mayo, number three,' she said and was able to relax again. In a few moments she would be held in soft welcoming arms. Darling Aunt Ana. There was no one in the world like her.

Dear Elena, thought Doña Ana Moural Carvelo de Contador. Next to her own three daughters there was no one in the world like her. Luisa simply did not deserve such a wonderful girl – but it was quite in character that Luisa should fail to appreciate her.

The girl had had a severe shock, with Vicente Vargas turning up from the dead without warning, and with a wife; and instead of giving her time to get over that, Luisa was pressing her to marry a man for whom she obviously had no inclination. If Luisa thought she, Ana, was going to lend her weight to push Elena into the match, she was very much mistaken. The duties of a sister-in-law did not extend to *that*.

Luisa must be mad, mad with family pride. Any woman in her senses would see that Carlos was not the man for Elena. He

62

was not nearly good enough for her. But he *was* a de Zurga, and she could imagine just how gratified Luisa would be if her one daughter reverted on marriage to her family name. Only a Moural had been good enough for Luisa to marry; now only a de Zurga was good enough for her daughter. What a lot of balderdash it was!

Doña Ana did not breathe a word of her opinions to Elena. She kept her thoughts to herself. Elena, in her own good time, if she wished, would discuss her affairs. Until then Doña Ana said nothing, and asked no questions. She filled the time with happy trivialities, trying to give Elena some of the pleasures which had lately been denied her.

Doña Ana had lost her husband and her brother Fernando in the same year. Her three daughters were all married, so she lived alone, amusing herself by visiting and entertaining and in addition making herself useful in a good many unobtrusive charitable ways that her acquaintances never suspected. And now she was taking as much pleasure in Elena's company as if one of her own daughters were staying with her.

Gregor Marint had stayed as long as was necessary at Valdoro. He had been quite happy to leave Vicente Vargas in charge and return to Varena. Happy? Satisfied about the estate affairs. would be more accurate. There was some undercurrent between Vargas and Señora Moural, of that he was certain, but Vargas must handle that himself. In this job, for the time he'd have to get used to that sort of thing from the ex-landowners' wives.

The Señora Moural disliked Vargas, that was obvious but there was something distinctly personal in it Marint thought. Quite as personal as her dislike for himself. She had known Vargas before; was the dislike bound up in some way with her dead son – or even with *La Hija*? Well, it was none of his business.

La Hija was in Varena. And *La Hija*, unlike her mother, did not actively dislike him now, that much he could tell. Beyond that he didn't care to venture an opinion; women were

63

incalculable creatures. Certainly at Valdoro she had tolerated him pretty well, but how far would that toleration extend?

There was only one way to find out. He called his secretary and asked for a telephone directory.

Marint, being a man of foresight, had not neglected to possess himself, in the course of a casual conversation with Carmela, of the name of the aunt with whom *La Hija* would be staying. She had better be on the phone, it would save a lot of trouble

Yes, there she was. Carvelo, Avenida de Mayo . . .

Marint sent his secretary away, and alone in his office picked up the telephone and asked for a private line. His ring was answered by a shy little voice which said, when he asked to speak to Señorita Moural: 'Just one moment, Señor. I will enquire.'

Of course, that was the maid.

He waited, but not for long. The receiver was picked up, and he heard *La Hija's* voice.

'Elena Moural speaking.'

It was cool, impersonal; her estate office tone.

'Good morning, Señorita Moural. Gregor Marint here. Do you like the opera?'

She could not quite hide her surprise, and was too taken aback to give more than the straight answer to his question.

'Yes. Very much.'

'Good. Then will you come with me? They're doing *L'Elisir d'Amore.*'

'Yes, I should like to.'

She had hardly hesitated.

'Fine. Are you free tomorrow evening?'

'Yes, I am.'

'Then I'll call for you.' He suggested a time, and she agreed. 'Until tomorrow evening, then.'

After considerable heart-searching Elena had written her mother a serious letter.

The situation which existed between herself and Carlos

64

could not be allowed to continue. He plainly hoped for an
engagement, but she knew that she did not want to marry him.
She was sorry not to be able to fall in with her mother's
wishes, and to cause such disappointment. Disappointment!
Doña Luisa would be in a state of cold fury, Elena knew that
only too well – and her next statement would only make
matters worse. She had decided while in Varena to look for a
suitable position. Their present circumstances were such that it
seemed the only sensible thing to do.

Elena said little more. There was no point in puffing out
the letter with excuses, nothing would make her mother feel
any better about it. She posted it with the feeling of having at
last done something decisive. No one else should settle her life
for her.

Carlos was now in Brazil on business; with luck there might
be time for her mother to write a letter which he would get on
his return, and she might be spared any more of Carlos's
courtship.

Then came the surprising call from General Marint. It was
totally unexpected, and she had no time to consider anything
but her own inclinations. When she told her aunt what she had
done Doña Ana did not even raise an eyebrow.

'The Opera! You'll love that, darling! What a good thing
your new dress will be ready in time. It will be perfect.'

Elena gazed at her astounded. 'But, Aunt Ana, I said it was
General Marint.'

'Well?'

'Don't you object to my going with him?'

Doña Ana smiled. 'Surely it's too late if I do? And why on
earth should I, if you don't? He's not taking me out! Why,
we're not living in the days of the *dueña*. When you were at
the university, didn't I let you go out alone, provided I knew
your escort? Now where is that directory?'

She began turning the pages of the telephone book.

'M. Madere . . . Malos . . . Marcos . . . Marino . . . bother!
He isn't in it. I suppose everyone would pester him if his
number was in the book.'

'Whose number?'

'General Marint's, of course! I shall have to ring the Ministry. Later, naturally.'

'But why? And surely they won't put you through to him?'

'I shall tell them to give him my name. He'll talk to me fast enough, if only to find out whether I'm going to forbid him to see you. And that's what you're wondering.

'In fact, I intend to invite him to come early and have a glass of wine with us. Then we will be able to take some of the wind out of Luisa's sails when she hears you've been out with him. I can say I had met and approved him. She'll condemn my opinion, but she won't be able to charge me with irresponsibility or you with disobedience. And to tell the truth, I want to meet the man!'

General Marint arrived with military punctuality.

Elena felt as nervous as a young girl just 'out' in society as she introduced him to her aunt. Doña Ana was, thank heaven, no snob; in many ways she was the antithesis of her sister-in-law. She must have a good first impression, Elena thought.

His manners could not be faulted. He was quite at ease and Doña Ana's smile was warm and welcoming.

'I can see that you're having a very good effect upon your niece,' he said. 'Señorita Moural is looking much fitter already.'

The hazel eyes under the dark brows gave Elena a brilliant look, warm with open admiration. Elena began to feel exhilarated. She had almost forgotten what it felt like to know she was looking her best and to enjoy being admired. But she must not let it go to her head; tonight they were going out in public, and she must remember not to be informal.

It was dark when they left the house, a warm velvety darkness scented with flowers. In the Avenida the street lamps were lit and a car was waiting at the kerb. It was a long black Citroën, a Ministry car with an Army driver who got out as they came down the steps and opened the door. Marint

66

handed her in and sat beside her.

During the drive into town the conversation flowed suprisingly easily.

As they neared the Opera House they fell silent. Elena was seized with sudden panic. It was three years since she had been seen in Varena society. How would these people react to seeing her with Marint? She would probably receive from them no more than glacial acknowledgement; this she wouldn't mind, she did not need their cordiality, but the unpleasant possibility was that she might receive politeness while Marint was ignored.

She was with him of her own free will, she would be humiliated if he was insulted by someone of her acquaintance. She knew her class only too well; their courtesy was exquisite, and when they chose to give a snub their rudeness was correspondingly devastating. Marint no doubt could give as good as he got, but it would be extremely disagreeable. She must use her wits to avoid people if necessary.

The car swept up to the forecourt and Elena forgot her apprehension and felt excitement rising in her. She might have been eighteen again, responding as she used to when her father headed the family party at the Opera season. He had been treated like a prince, everyone knew him, everything was organized for him. He had been a fine-looking man with a wonderful personality, she had been so proud to be his daughter.

Already Marint was guiding her through the crush of people. The foyer was full of colour, brilliantly lit by crystal chandeliers. It had been redecorated and looked as fine as she remembered it before the Revolution. The people, too, were gay and smart: one could forget that there had ever been fighting and destruction in the streets of Varena.

One of the Opera House officials appeared beside them.

'General Marint, this way, please.'

He escorted them to their seats in the stalls. Elena began to feel at ease, the seats on either side of them were already occupied by people who were strangers to her. Above and to her right was the box where she had often sat beside her father. A box! If Marint had been the upstart her mother considered him he would have booked a box to impress her – and would have virtually compromised her in the eyes of her society by so doing.

She took a deep breath; that was one hurdle passed before she had realized its existence. Marint had booked precisely the right seats. It was a good omen for the evening.

She gave herself up to enjoyment of the opera. She was aware that beside her Marint was appreciating it as much as she was. He was familiar with it, he understood Italian quite well, he was revelling in the humour.

As he led her out during the interval they exchanged views on the performance. Interesting as their conversation was, Elena was conscious that they were not unnoticed. Marint was a public figure and she had expected him to be recognized. But the reaction was not what she had foreseen. This upper-class audience was positively eager to acknowledge him, and several times Elena caught the expression in a woman's eyes which said, 'That's a very attractive man. I'd like to be in your shoes.' This had the delightful effect of reinforcing her confidence.

When the performance was over, a way was made for them to the main doors.

Outside the air was cooler, the top of the steps above the forecourt looked out on to the Plaza, a patch of darkness starred with lamps and slashed with headlights. Below them was a group of press photographers; waiting for celebrities, thought Elena idly, some film stars, an international beauty, a tycoon or two, no doubt.

Marint spoke to her and she turned to answer him. Flash bulbs popped surprisingly close. The car was at the foot of the steps. He handed her in, but before he could follow one of the press men approached him.

'General Marint, won't you tell us the name of your charming companion?'

From her seat in the car Elena saw him turn, flashing a wicked grin, and heard his reply quite plainly. 'No!' he said firmly. 'You find your own girl friends, and leave me to look after mine!'

There was a loud chuckle from the bystanders, in which the press man joined, and then Marint was sitting beside her and they were driving off. Elena fought a desire to giggle; no one she had ever known would have made such a retort. They both pretended she had not heard it.

'Would you like some fresh air?' he asked. He leaned forward to speak to the driver. 'Take us to the park, Sergeant.'

Varena's central park was a favourite place for evening strolls. Marint stopped the car when they were on one of the driveways.

'You can return the car and go off duty now, Sergeant,' he said. 'I'll take a taxi from here.'

The tree-lined avenues were spacious, cool and fresh after the crowded Opera House. There were plenty of people strolling in couples or family groups, for in Riqueza, particularly in summer, it was usual to rest in the afternoon and keep late hours in the cool of the evening.

They sauntered along like the others, talking easily, Marint amusing Elena with a turn of dry humour which she had only just discovered in him. After a while they reached a part of the park where the formal avenues with their geometrically planted flower-beds gave way to open land.

There in the daytime children played at will, and itinerant vendors were free to set up their stands. At some distance a number of booths seemed to be plying a busy trade, and just beyond the end of the avenue a doughnut seller was waiting for custom. His stand was very simple; it consisted of a small trestle table and a portable brazier over which smoked a huge cauldron of frying oil.

'Have you ever had *churros* straight from the pot?'

'Only once or twice,' she admitted. 'When I was a student,' she explained.

'I see! The dreadful debauchery of the university! Would you like some now?'

Her eyes showed her surprise and then began to dance with

laughter. She felt frivolous, a little crazy.

'Yes, please.'

The doughnut man showed no surprise. He got on with the job, squeezing the soft mixture from a bag, making circles of it straight into the hot oil. They sizzled away, turning pale gold, and in a couple of minutes he hooked them out, tossed them in sugar, and threaded them one by one on to a thin peeled stick from a pile on the table. He twisted the pliant stick into a loop to keep them on, and handed it to Marint.

Elena took off her gloves and put them into her handbag as they waited for the doughnuts to cool a little. Marint, with a solemn face and amusement in his eyes, offered her one, then took one himself and bit into it with obvious appreciation.

He stood there, munching doughnuts and then licking his fingers in a way which was not coarse but somehow raffish.

'I didn't book a table for supper as I didn't know if you'd like a smart place or prefer a quiet one.' He paused. 'Where shall we go? It's your choice, though from the look of you now I could almost suggest a round of the stands!'

'That's a good idea. Let's try them all!'

She felt free. It was just like being at university again, where the old conventions were winked at and she could forget her position and the need for constant decorum. Did she like Marint because he never considered such things? Men were lucky, it was easier for them to make their own rules. Did he think she would never unbend? He was wrong. She was going to enjoy this mad outing.

The booths were lit, some with flares, some with lamps and they crossed the dark rough ground, he with a hand under her elbow, going from one pool of light to another.

At each counter they sampled the wares and had a word or two with the vendors, generally man and wife, all friendly peasant folk. No one cared, least of all Marint, that beside the other customers the two of them looked like peacocks in a barnyard.

That he was invariably recognized bothered him not at all. They ate a wild variety of savoury snacks — fish, cheese, olives,

70

slices of sausage – then progressed to sugary cakes, little sweet biscuits, and lumps of candy.

At length they strolled out of the park and found a little café-bar, simple, clean and quiet. They went in for coffee. Marint ordered a glass of brandy apiece as well, and they sat there at a corner table, sipping their drinks.

What fun it had been! Elena thought. She would never have dreamed of such an evening. With Carlos, of course, it would have been quite impossible. The Opera, which he would not have enjoyed very much, would have been followed by supper booked at a smart restaurant, where everything would be predictable and conversation would be superficial and limited.

But to follow the formal pleasures of the Opera with the round of the park booths as if they were poor children out on a treat – that was spontaneous, unexpected, and with Gregor Marint, had all the fun of a fiesta. She could not remember having laughed so much for years.

Now he was looking at her silently, and she had the odd feeling that they were quite alone, that nothing outside the circle of their own table was real or significant.

She looked, not at his eyes, but at his hands. At the short blunt fingers with square well-kept nails, at the play of bone and muscle under the brown skin, and suddenly remembered the strength of them, how they could hold a horse like Diablo in check, of how they had grasped her when he had kissed her . . .

Realization flooded over her that now she would not want to resist. And he had been quite right: she had been denying her emotions for far too long.

Her love for Vicente was past and over, the pain awakened by his return was fading. He belonged to someone else. She had hardly thought of him for the past few days. It was strange that all at once she had found acceptance, and her love had changed to a calm affection that she could keep with a clear conscience, remembering him as a part of her life that was behind her as was all the heartache that their love had caused.

But this man opposite her, whose searching eyes she could not meet, was a man of great attraction. Although her life was changing, Marint was the last man on earth she should let her affections get entangled with. She knew that after the emotional desert she had been in, she was vulnerable. And this man had some terrific magnetism which made him very dangerous.

She pushed the thoughts aside. Tonight she was enjoying herself. No harm in that, as long as she knew what she was doing. At present he was charming; so much the better, as long as she knew she was being charmed.

They left the café; Marint hailed a taxi, and she got in.

'Avenida de Mayo, number three.' And he was beside her.

It had been a good evening, Gregor Marint was thinking. He was attracted to the girl. It wasn't just her beauty, he had known other women nearly as beautiful. He sensed that she was temperamentally at the same time more simple and much more complex than any other woman of his experience. He guessed that hidalgo tradition and a modern attitude of mind were two opposing forces which must often pull her uncomfortably in two different directions.

Which would win? Her future, her happiness might depend on that. Riqueza hadn't got much time now for a girl who insisted on clinging to the past. She would probably try to compromise, and he doubted whether that would be successful either.

But what a waste, to be thinking of such things when he was alone in a taxi with her. He could see her quite clearly in the shifting light from street lamps and passing cars, and he let his eyes rest on her face admiringly. She looked uncertain whether to smile at him or not.

'I really believe,' he said levelly, 'that you think I am a cross between Ghengis Khan and Attila the Hun. Why, any *Norte-Americano* would give you more reason for alarm than I have!'

72

Now she smiled. 'What do you mean?'

'Don't you know that a kiss in a cab is part of the *Yanqui* way of life?' he teased. 'But here I am sitting in my corner, true to my Riquezan upbringing.'

'If I thought so badly of you I would hardly have accepted your invitation.'

'That's true.'

She leaned her head back. Her eyelids drooped.

'You're sleepy. I'm not surprised. My shoulder would be more comfortable than the corner of the cab. Won't you pretend you're my favourite niece? She always says she needs a rest after one of our orgies at the park booths.'

Undecided, she said nothing.

'But of course she trusts me more than you do.'

After the slightest pause her voice came, soft but clear. 'I trust you.'

He stretched out his arm. 'Sit closer.'

She moved nearer and leaned against him. His arm was behind her, but he was careful to keep his hand on the car seat, not to embrace her.

She was a high-bred nervous filly and needed careful schooling. Her cheek was against his shoulder, the black cloud of her hair below his head. Her body was slight and warm, he could feel it moving gently against his with every breath.

One slim hand lay relaxed upon her knee, he took it in his and she did not draw it away. He raised it to his lips and kissed the back of it. 'Have lunch with me.'

'Yes . . . when?'

'Three days from now. I'll call for you.'

'Very well.'

Her night-black hair was only inches from his lips. He bent and put his mouth gently upon it. It was smooth and soft as silk, and smelt faintly of flowers. But she was a flower . . .

'*Linda flor* . . .' he murmured. '*Flor de la noche* . . .'

He felt a slight movement of the hand in his, and raising it again to his lips he pressed three kisses into her palm.

'There — a kiss for each day until we meet.'

He glanced out of the window. 'We're nearly there.'

He handed her out of the taxi and waited while she found her key. She turned and smiled at him.

'Good night. And thank you for a lovely evening.'

'You are the loveliest thing in it. Good night, *Hija de Valdoro.*'

CHAPTER SIX

Carlos de Zurga, arriving back in Varena from Brazil, decided that his personal affairs must now take precedence over business. There was no need for him to go to the office that day; he could not afford any more delay with Elena, he must see her as soon and as often as possible. Away from Valdoro there would be much more opportunity for courtship – it would be a bad setback if she returned there before he had won her consent.

Why not drive from the airport straight to the Avenida de Mayo? With luck he would find her in, and be able to take her out to lunch. A *tête-à-tête* in a quiet corner of an expensive restaurant, that would be the way to start.

But she was not in, it appeared.

'I'm sorry, Señor de Zurga,' Josefina the maid faltered, 'but she's not here. Nor – nor is Señorita Moural.'

Carlos cursed under his breath. 'When will they be back?' he demanded.

'I really don't know, Señor. Doña Ana is having lunch with Señor Vasquez.'

'And Señorita Moural? Isn't she with Señora Carvelo?'

'Oh no, Señor, she was lunching out. But I am sure the Señora knew and approved. He has been here before.'

'*He* has? *Who* has?' Carlos seized the girl's arm and shook her. '*Who*?'

Josefina stared at him wide-eyed, too startled by his anger to speak for a moment. Then she pulled herself together.

'Why, it was the General, Señor. General Gregor Marint.'

Gregor Marint had been five minutes late calling for Elena. She had not expected that, and she was even more surprised to see, when he came striding into the hall, that he was wearing his uniform and decorations. He saluted her with a broad smile and gave a quick explanation.

'I had an official engagement this morning, and it took much longer than was scheduled. As this house is on the way back, I thought I would save time by calling for you before I changed. I shan't keep you waiting for more than a few minutes.'

Elena had not seen him in uniform since his arrival at Valdoro. It brought home to her how her attitude to him had changed.

Then she had been suspicious, antagonistic, apprehensive and critical; now her feelings were of warmth, of friendship, even of admiration. She had been looking forward to this meeting, wondering if their talk would be at all confidential, if she might learn something more about him. She knew so little, and she wanted to know so much.

A staff car whisked them into town, to his flat. There had been no mention of his parents at any time — were they dead now, did he live alone? Perhaps the flat was the nearest thing to home that he knew. Or did he have a house somewhere out of town as well?

Somehow she had never thought of that. He had always seemed to her a man on the move, with no ties, no encumbrances. But where did he keep his horses? He must have horses. How silly of her! They would be in the stables at the Army barracks.

The staff car had reached a district near the Government offices, where large, solidly respectable houses that had once been owned by wealthy families had recently been converted into flats.

'With my batman,' Marint was saying, 'I can change in three minutes flat.'

He got out of the car, and when she made no move to follow he turned and put his head through the door.

'Aren't you coming? Everyone round here knows my car,

you'll collect a lot of stares in three minutes. You'll be more comfortable inside.'

Riquezans are inquisitive and uninhibited, and she did not relish being the centre of attention in such circumstances, so she joined him and, followed by the driver, they entered the building.

A plain hall, a self-operated lift in which the three of them went up to the sixth floor. Everything was simple, there was no fuss. Elena had half expected to see a porter or a floor attendant who was a disguised bodyguard lurking nearby. The door had no name plate, only a number; everything was plain, unguarded and anonymous.

Marint let them in with his key. Four doors opened from a small tiled hall, and he showed her through the one on the extreme left. The driver, who apparently doubled as batman, went through the door on the far right.

'You can set the clock on me — three minutes!' Marint said, unbuckling his belt and holster as he went out.

Elena looked around. This was his living room, she guessed that the bedroom was on the far right, with a kitchen and bathroom between.

This looked like thorough-going bachelor quarters, there was no sign of a woman about, except that everything was clean and tidy. She didn't think he was a man to make much clutter — his military training, perhaps. A daily woman would have no trouble in keeping this in good order.

There were large comfortable chairs, but she did not sit down. She strolled over to the table, which was set in a good light under the single, wide window. A few maps were lying on it.

On a smaller table to one side was a board set with chessmen; a game was evidently in progress. Of course, he was famous as a military tactician, chess would be his game.

On the walls some old military prints contrasted with a striking painting of horsemen on the pampa: this picture was the only really modern note in the room.

One wall was lined with bookshelves. She had not expected

to see many books, and they gave the room a lived-in look, an atmosphere of permanence. She glanced along them. One could learn a lot from a persons taste in books.

Her first surprise was to find they were not all Spanish titles. A large group were French, and of these a few looked like college textbooks. She took out one -- Corneille's *Le Cid*. It had 'Gregor Marint' written on the flyleaf in a rather youthful hand, and underneath the name of a provincial college of high reputation. The book fell open at a page on which a couplet was marked in pencil.

'Et l'on peut me réduire à vivre sans bonheur,
Mais non pas me résoudre à vivre sans honneur.'

she read, and murmured to herself, 'I can be reduced to living without happiness, but not forced to live without honour.'

So that was the young Gregor Marint. She put *Le Cid* back and looked further.

A complete row of English books caught her eye. Some were standard military treatises; there were technical books and an English-Spanish dictionary of technical terms; memoirs of a British general and several English books on World War Two; and at the end a mixed bag -- Shakespeare, an anthology of poetry, *Seven Pillars of Wisdom*, and a large beautifully illustrated book on guns, cheek by jowl with a lovely folio of reprints from Audubon's *Birds of America*.

The catholicity of his tastes intrigued and appealed to her. She looked at the folio, but her mind was only half on the pictures. For days Gregor Marint had been dominating her thoughts, and she had been fighting the attraction she knew he had for her. He had come to stand for everything her family hated. But that was so unfair -- he was a man of education and ideals. It was a mere accident that his viewpoint and his ways were different from theirs. Why shouldn't she be friends with him? Friends? She thought of the drive home from the Opera. and her heart leaped within her.

The door opened and Marint stood there. He was wearing not the ubiquitous white summer suit, but one of biscuit-coloured linen, with a white shirt and a narrow tie in a shade of tan, and brown leather shoes. There was a well-pressed spruceness and spotlessness about him which might have made another man look a dandy. In his case it seemed to accentuate his masculinity.

'On time?' he asked.

'I don't know. It seemed like no time at all. I was looking at your books. I hope you don't mind.'

'Not at all. Shall we go?'

The driver took them in the staff car to a restaurant, and Marint then dismissed him. The place was new to Elena. The whole block looked as if it had been rebuilt since the war, and externally it was fresh, smart and attractive. The decoration inside was a modern version of the Spanish-Riquezan style. Marint caught her appreciative look.

'The food's good, too,' he remarked.

Their table had been booked. It was not in the dining-room but on a covered terrace overlooking a patio, so they had shade and open air, and as the tables there were few, there was more quiet and privacy than in the main part of the restaurant. It was a delightful spot, such as one did not expect to find in the heart of the city.

The terrace was framed by arches, the supporting pillars of which were entwined with climbing plants, and round the sides of the patio were long troughs of brown earthenware filled with flowering shrubs, their blossoms splashing the place with colour and filling the air with their scent. From some of the arches were hanging large cages which held parrots, macaws and cockatoos whose vivid plumage, red and blue, yellow, rosy pink or iridescent green, seemed more brilliant than the flowers.

'You like the place?' Marint asked.

'It's charming. And the birds — '

'Are fine as long as they don't join in the conversation.'

Elena felt relaxed and happy. She gazed out over the patio. He mustn't suspect how much he was beginning to interest her. Just to see him was in an odd way stimulating.

To say Carlos was affronted gave no idea at all of his mental condition. Rage and jealousy were now boiling within him, and he felt quite unable to stay in Doña Ana's house trying to wait calmly for Elena's return.

He drove into town and found himself parking outside his club. He would go in and have a drink — at this time of day the chances were that it would be deserted and he would be able to sit quietly and think of his next move.

At first he thought the club room was empty. Then he caught sight of Joaquín Torres stretched out in an armchair in one corner.

'Olá, Carlos! Come and join me!'

Carlos hid his unwillingness and did so. He had known Joaquín since boyhood, and had never liked him much. He was too quick, too perceptive.

'Some wine, Carlos? Or your favourite bourbon?'

'Neither, thanks. A brandy.'

'Two cognacs, Juan!' Joaquín called to the barman.

'Well, I haven't seen you lately, *amigo!* What have you been up to?'

'I've been in Brazil.'

'*Ay*! You should have been in Varena, with your pretty cousin paying the capital a visit at long last.'

'I have several pretty cousins,' replied Carlos shortly.

'Lucky man! I meant, of course, the prettiest and most elusive — Señorita Moural! From her picture in the *Gazetta* I should guess she is even lovelier than when I last saw her — which was far too long ago.'

Carlos stared at him. 'Her picture?'

Had his father, in his enthusiasm for the match, let their plans leak out? Had he made some unofficial announcement which the newspapers had seized upon? That would be enough to drive Elena in the other direction — perhaps that was why she had refused him.

The barman had placed a glass on the table beside Carlos, and hiding his confusion he took up his drink.

'Don't say you haven't seen it?' Joaquín was continuing

smoothly. 'It was most interesting. Juan! Find a copy of yesterday's *Noticia*, you must have one somewhere.'

Joaquín went on talking; Carlos answered in monosyllables, hardly listening. Juan returned, and handed Joaquín a copy of the *Noticia de Varena.*

Joaquín pushed it casually across to Carlos. 'There you are. Inside, the gossip page. "Argus" is on form this week.'

Carlos unfolded the newspaper, and the photograph leaped at him like a blow between the eyes.

Elena and Marint — side by side — smiling at each other. The caption underneath read: 'Señorita Moural and General Marint leaving the Opera House.'

Nombre de Jésus, what would people think? Everyone would have seen it, and drawn their own conclusions. Then he realized that was not all. 'Argus' had appended his own comments. He sat there appalled and read them.

'A piquant situation is illustrated by the picture on the left of this column. Our dashing General Gregor Marint', — Carlos could not suppress a snort of disgust. The phrases these journalists used! — *protagonist of Land Reform, and now the Minister at the head of that Department, has had occasion recently on the President's instructions to enforce in person Sequestration Orders on the largest estancias in the country.*

'One of these was Valdoro, long in possession of the Moural family. It would seem that one of the Mourales, at least, does not cherish any animosity towards the General himself. Could this be called a truce, a victory, or a conquest, one wonders? From the picture one might assume that honours are equally divided. And the opera they seem to have enjoyed so much? "L'Elisir d'Amore"!"

Carlos sat silent, trying to fight down his fury and shame. The whole city must be laughing. Where was the de Zurga and Moural pride, their reputation, if one of their women was allowed to be so friendly with such scum?

' . . . a truce, a victory, or a conquest . . . .' the words screamed at him. He looked at the picture. They were smiling at each other. *Cuerpo de Jesús!* He looked ready to possess

81

her! And she — Carlos's hands clenched tighter — she never smiled at *him* like that.

With one swift broad sweep of his hand he thrust the paper from him on to the floor. Then without a word strode from the room.

He had had enough. He could not and would not endure this situation. Somewhere in Varena Elena and Marint were together. He would find them.

'But why did you join the Army?'

Elena was quite at ease with him now, so much so that she had been questioning him about himself. Whether from tact or preference she had touched on nothing controversial; she had wanted to know about his early life.

He had told her. Better for her to have an honest version than the garbled stuff the papers printed. And she didn't expect him to have led an hidalgo's life. But there was nothing in his origins of which he need be ashamed.

His maternal grandfather had been a landowner in a small way — a little ranch, nothing on the Valdoro scale — but he wasn't exactly poor. His mother had refused the husband her parents intended for her, and had eloped with a city merchant some years older than herself. They had three children, himself and two younger daughters.

'I was six when my father died,' he went on, 'and my mother found herself left with the three of us, and swindled out of her money by my father's business partner. My grandparents heard of it, and took us home. They were a fine pair, generous and open-hearted; there was never a word of recrimination or reproach. My grandfather gave me a good education, though I must admit I enjoyed holidays on the ranch more than school or college.'

'And then what happened?'

'They wanted to send me to university. But there was a limit to what I could accept from my grandfather — possibly I felt it more because he was so generous and never expected my gratitude. He would have bought me into one of the

82

professions if I'd let him. But apart from the money angle. I had no clear idea of what I wanted to do. So I made a clean break, left home, and knocked about earning my living in a dozen different ways.'

'What ways?'

'Cattle-driving, horse-breaking, mining — anything I fancied. I was never out of a job.'

'But why did you join the Army?'

He knew what she meant. It was bad enough for an educated man to take jobs where muscle was more important than brain, but to join up as a private soldier — in those days you couldn't sink any lower. The ranks were rabble, any volunteer was taken and no questions asked. The Army was a refuge for criminals and a meal ticket for the starving and unemployable.

He sat for a moment, remembering just how it happened.

'It was quite by accident. I'd been doing some horse-breaking and I left the ranch and reached a village at the same time that a detachment of soldiers came through. I saw one of the privates being brutally treated by the sergeant. And everyone accepted it — everyone — the soldiers, the man himself, the villagers — no one found it wrong or even unusual. The more I thought about it the more I saw that it was no way to run an army. For that matter I had decided, long before, that the whole country was mismanaged. The system was feudal, it was inhuman, and it was wasteful. If we were to survive as a nation we needed to catch up with the twentieth century, and fast.'

Elena said nothing, but nodded encouragingly.

'The politicians who were in a position to do something about it were doing nothing. To give them a push one would need money and influence. I had neither. But the Army might be different. That might be influenced from the bottom up, so to speak. I thought it over, and decided it was possible.'

She was listening to him as if he was an oracle.

'So you joined as a private — to reform the Army!'

'Put like that it sounds ambitious. But the jobs I had tried

83

hadn't really satisfied me, and this seemed worth a bit of effort. I was sure I could make my way and clean things up as I went along. I was a bit arrogant, I suppose. Without money, unless the rules were radically changed, I knew I could never get a commission, but I secretly hoped there might be a way round even that in time.'

'And that was the beginning of the Army Reforms? I know something about them now — it's fantastic!'

'Not really. After a certain point it just gathered momentum.'

'But how did you start?'

'The first part was quite easy. As you know, at that time men only volunteered as an alternative to starvation or prison. The quartermasters were crooked, the food was foul — but it was life to a man who had no hope of a job and wasn't clever enough to steal without being caught. Once I was in, I wasn't in very exalted company. In those days if you stood up straight and kept your uniform clean you were a corporal, automatically, I got my stripe in two days.'

'And then what?'

'Then I had ten men under me, and I told them we were going to be the smartest squad in the Riquezan Army.'

'And what did they say?'

'They laughed. They'd been laughing at me for two days because I kept myself clean. And I let them. But now they were my squad I made a bargain with them.'

'What was that?'

'I offered to fight them, one by one, and they agreed that if I could beat them all they'd do things my way.'

She gazed at him with renewed astonishment. 'Fight them? How? What with?'

He grinned as he spoke. 'With my fists, of course! Did you expect swords or pistols? This wasn't a quarrel, just a friendly fight!'

'What happened?' she said weakly.

He shrugged. 'They did things my way. The next morning we were the cleanest, ugliest squad in the Army. You never

84

saw such a collection of black eyes and bright buttons.'

The delightful girl was actually giggling.

'Tell me some more. What happened next? Did you have to black every eye in the Army?'

He chuckled. 'No. I farmed out a lot of it later on. But I've talked too much about myself already. Don't you like the *gazpacho*?'

'Yes, it's delicious.'

'When you've finished it you can tell me about yourself for a change.'

I would rather talk about you, Elena thought. There was so much she wanted to know. Everyone seemed to know more about him than she did. She kept discovering more sides to his character. Militant idealist. Ambitious self-improver. Ruthless commander. He was all of these, and probably more. He wasn't in the least like any of the men she had known.

He was unconventional; he had no respect for traditions; one could not be neutral towards him. She had started by detesting him – and now – she mustn't think along those lines. He was interesting, leave it at that.

'Tell me – your name?' she asked. 'It's not a bit Spanish.'

'No. My father's grandfather – or great grandfather – I don't know which generation – was an immigrant from Central Europe. He was a fine old mixture; as far as European blood is concerned, you name it, I've probably got it from him. He settled here, and from then on the Marints married Spaniards, as far as I know. I've never heard of any Indian ancestry, but if there were, it wouldn't bother me. What's one more strain to a mongrel?'

She smiled thoughtfully. 'You can't speak of people as mongrels. They are – what they are. For me, the only pedigrees that have any interest are those of horses and cattle – they're important. But people aren't animals.'

'All the same, it would give you a shock if you found you were mixed,' he said easily. 'You wouldn't like your fine pedigree spoiled.'

She did not hide her surprise at the remark, and saε

considering it. 'I suppose it would be a shock at first, because I should wonder if I'd inherited any tendencies of which I wasn't aware. Once I'd got used to it and convinced myself I was still the same person, I hope it wouldn't matter to me. Besides, that's unfair. It's a very different thing having something sprung on you which you know nothing about, from growing up knowing it, or the possibility of it.'

He leaned towards her, holding her with the look in his bright bold eyes. 'Would you be sitting with me here now if you *knew*, and knew that everyone knew, that *I* was mixed? Wouldn't it make a difference?'

Why was he asking? Was it just curiosity at her reactions?

'Do you think I'm mean-minded, and such a snob? I thought you knew that I'm not so prejudiced.'

'I do. I think you'd still be here, but I don't know whether you'd feel quite comfortable about it. You don't know much about me in any respect, do you? Haven't you thought it might be unwise to be friendly with me?'

Thank heaven, here was the waiter with their steaks. It would give her a few moments to consider her answer. When they were served she replied as coolly as she could.

'You sound as if you want to get rid of me. I insist on finishing my lunch.'

He laughed. 'You have quite the wrong impression! I enjoy your company, I want more of it. But I'm trying to be fair to you. Your aunt doesn't object to me -- but your mother, when she hears of this -- I imagine there will be trouble for you. It hadn't mattered before, but now I intend to see you often I must know how much her disapproval will affect you.'

'I intend to see you often . . .' her heart leaped at the words. A strange elation flowed through her. So they were to be friends, this was not just an isolated meeting, the product of a passing interest. She was happy, it was what she had longed for, the reassurance that he was not merely amusing himself.

He persisted. 'Will it matter so much? Must I change my plans?'

'No!' The word burst out. 'My mother disapproves of you – yes! But she doesn't rule me. I live my own life!'

'I intend to see you often . . . .' She smiled to herself. He had not even asked her if she would be agreeable. But why should he? They each knew they enjoyed the other's company, so why pretend? That was one of Gregor's characteristics: he never pretended.

'Are you going to marry young de Zurga?'

The question startled her by its sheer irrelevance. Nothing had been farther from her mind than marrying Carlos. She tried to collect her thoughts.

'How did you know he wanted to .,. .'

'I used my head. He hadn't been to see you for years, then he suddenly appeared with a lawyer in tow. The atmosphere was too convivial for litigation, so it had to be a marriage contract. The choice was between yourself and Señorita de Burgos. I read the signs, and my money was on you. And I was right.'

'Yes, you were right,' she agreed soberly.

'Well, are you going to marry him?'

'No.'

'That's good.'

'Why?'

'Because he wouldn't suit you. I could say he wasn't good enough for you, but I could think of a hell of a lot of men who come into that category – and very few who don't.'

'Be careful. I might take that as a compliment.'

Someone was approaching their table. It was the restaurant manager.

'Forgive me, Señor General. I do not wish to disturb you, but there is a gentleman who is asking to see you. He says it is urgent.'

'Did he give his name?'

'No, General, he refused. Shall I call the police?'

'Does he look dangerous?'

The man shrugged unhappily. 'He looks angry, General.'

87

'Well, I don't suppose he'll shoot me here. There's not much chance to escape if he wants to get away, and it's not public enough for someone who has a mind to be a martyr. I'll see him.'

Elena was horrified. She knew that Gregor had enemies, but that he could accept the thought of being murdered, and calmly assess the possibilities — it sent a chill through her. But she had no time to think about it, for a man was shouldering his way through a group of waiters, thrusting them autocratically aside. In one shocked second she saw it was Carlos de Zurga.

He was very pale, his eyes dark pits with a speck of cold light in each; his lips were pressed tightly together and pulled down at the corners so that his face had almost the appearance of a mask. If he comes any closer, Elena thought, I shall smell a reek of hatred and violence.

He glanced at Elena and then stared full at Marint. On his forehead and upper lip were tiny beads of sweat. He said nothing.

'Sit down, de Zurga.' Gregor's voice was cool and casual. The manager came forward and spoke.

'So you know the gentleman, General. That is good. Will he perhaps be joining you?'

Gregor's voice was now as cold as his look. 'The gentleman will not be staying long enough to eat anything.'

Carlos stood over them, his mouth twitching, his eyes blazing with hate and fury.

'I said sit down, de Zurga. If you have something to say, say it quietly. We don't want any fuss in Señorita Moural's presence.'

Carlos pulled out the chair abruptly, sat down. Elena hoped that from where the other diners sat it would look like a friendly conversation.

'How convenient for you, to be able to shelter behind the presence of a lady!'

'How mistaken of me to call you a gentleman. Have you anything else to say?'

'Simply this. Stop thrusting your attentions on my cousin! Her family consider rightly that you are not fit company for her, and it is damaging to her reputation to be seen with you. You will therefore not meet her or speak to her again at any time, for any reason.'

His voice was hoarse and rough, his breath smelled of brandy.

'Carlos, how dare you —'

Elena's outburst was checked by Marint.

'One moment. At present this is between the two of us.'

Then he spoke slowly and deliberately, his eyes fixed on the other man with an expression of cold anger and undisguised contempt.

'Presumably, de Zurga, you consider you have some right to interfere, but let me tell you this. You may be a very fine cock on your own dunghill, but don't think you can come crowing over me!' Then he added: 'Out of respect for your cousin I'll amend that to "cock in your own barnyard", but the thought's the same.'

An angry flush was creeping up Carlos's face. 'You can't insult me —'

Marint smiled. 'It's difficult, I grant you. So much that's unpleasant is true of you. But I advise you to leave before I'm tempted. There's a great deal I could say.'

'I shall leave as soon as I have made the situation clear to you, and Señorita Moural will leave with me.'

'Carlos!'

'Not unless she chooses.'

Elena could keep out of the quarrel no longer. 'Carlos your behaviour is insufferable! I will not be dictated to! If I choose to go out with anyone it is my affair, and you will keep your opinions to yourself. Now go away and mind your own business.'

Marint watched the tension developing between them, still smiling a little, his look sardonic.

'Do you think I shall leave you here with him? Everyone knows his reputation! You must have taken leave of your senses! If you have no respect for the family name, I have, and I don't intend to have it sniggered over by the gutterpress of Varena. You will come with me, at once!'

'I shall not.'

'You can't win, de Zurga,' remarked Marint. 'The lady doesn't want to go. If you try to – persuade her, you will cause a scene, and that will make good copy. Do you want to feature in tomorrow's *Noticia*?'

Carlos slowly turned to him. As he looked at Marint the bitter rage and animosity which showed in his face was almost tangible, it seemed to vibrate in the air between them.

'What I have already seen in the *Noticia* has disgusted me. That you should have the audacity to appear in public with my – my cousin! I warn you, Marint, don't repeat it! In future, leave her alone! You may think your present position gives you the whip hand, but if necessary I shall certainly find some way to teach you to respect birth and breeding.'

'Don't threaten me, boy!' Marint's voice was low and scornful. 'Take your eighteenth-century posturing somewhere else and leave me to my meal. You're giving me indigestion.'

For a long moment Carlos said nothing. Then: 'This isn't the end of the matter. Don't think I'm going to let it rest here. Elena – '

He turned to her and, as she made no move, his hand went out towards her wrist.

'Don't do that!' Marint's voice was hard and cold as ice, and Carlos's hand stopped in mid-air. Abruptly he got to his feet, pushing the chair back with a grating clatter.

Carlos looked at Elena. 'If you can give me your attention for one moment I would like to tell you that there is a letter from your mother awaiting you at the Avenida de Mayo.'

With that he stalked off the terrace.

'Delightful fellow,' Marint remarked. 'He certainly knows how to choose his time and place to insult a man!'

'What do you mean?' Elena whispered.

Now the scene was over she felt not only enraged but bitterly humiliated and ashamed. She found she was trembling,

90

and clasped her hands tightly together in her lap to hide the fact from Gregor Marint.

'Mean? I mean he's lucky his teeth aren't half-way down his throat, the impudent puppy! And for someone so concerned about your reputation, so keen to keep your name out of the papers, he was taking a chance!'

Elena's mind refused to work. 'I still don't understand — '

'Madre de Dios! Do you think I let men insult me as he did? Do you think I'd care a damn if tomorrow's paper had a headline "Marint in café brawl"? But what else would they print? Wouldn't the reporters be only too pleased to say we were fighting over you? And to invent their own reasons? What do you think they'd make of our relationship? It would be a field-day for the gossips — especially the dirtier-minded ones — they would really enjoy themselves!'

Elena felt her stomach turn over. She was still not used to the fact that, whatever Marint did, was likely to be publicized; the result of their visit to the Opera had been bad enough, and she was not surprised that Carlos had resented it. But if there had been a public quarrel her reputation would have been in ribbons in twenty-four hours. And he had thought of that, and endured Carlos's unforgivable behaviour for her sake!

Marint's jaw was set, his mouth hard with barely suppressed rage and resentment.

'I'm sorry — I didn't realize — '

'He's lucky I'm not as low as he thinks I am! In that case his precious family name would be distinctly tarnished by now, and he'd be in hospital. *Dios!* I eat boys like that for breakfast!'

Elena felt near to tears. 'What can I say? I feel responsible, as he's my relative, but he had absolutely no right — it was appalling behaviour — '

She stretched her hand out to him across the table. 'I know it was unpardonable. I apologize for him — I don't know what else to say — I am sorry, Gregor.'

The scowl smoothed out, he looked surprised, then he was smiling. His fingers closed over hers, they were hard and strong and warm.

'What did you say?'

'I said I was sorry.'

'You said something else.'

It was only then that she realized that she had used his name.

'I said "I'm sorry, Gregor",' she repeated quietly.

'*Querida*!' His voice was low and tender. 'Why, you're trembling! Don't let this upset you! I'm furious, but with him, not you – and with myself, because I couldn't give him what he asked for. But it was worth it to hear you say that, unasked.'

Her hand was tingling at the clasp of his fingers. Strange sensations were pulsing in her body, her heart was beating faster, she felt relaxed yet at the same time stimulated. His eyes had a look of anticipation, of longing mingled with triumph, she was not sure what it meant.

The waiter was coming, she had to draw her hand away, but Gregor still looked at her, she did not have to see his face to know his eyes were on her. Their plates were removed, and as the sweet was served they sat in silence. Elena waited for Marint to lead the conversation; the atmosphere between them was too intimate, too fraught with questions and desires for small talk to be anything but an anti-climax to her.

'Say it again, *linda flor.*'

He poured some more wine into her glass. She smiled with joy at his sweet name for her. No pretence, she thought, we both know what he means.

She looked at him, and saw a man who held her happiness in the hollow of his hand. He was the centre of her thoughts and her emotions, he tugged at the very fibres of her being with an attraction she could no longer resist. She was stunned by the sudden knowledge that she loved him. It was not his friendship she wanted. She wanted his arms about her, his lips on hers, she wanted his love.

'Gregor,' she murmured.

He raised his glass to her.

'*Ay, querida*! I have been waiting for that. That's one barrier the less between us.'

'Barrier?' She shook her head. 'We had to get to know each other before we could be friends - that takes time — but I didn't know there were barriers.'

'You didn't know? Why, you're surrounded by them. They're not all of your making, but you've accepted them, nevertheless. Until now, that is. You're imprisoned by old conventions, even though you've fooled yourself into thinking you're a modern emancipated woman. I'm hoping that between us we'll manage to make a breach in them.'

'You're exaggerating, Gregor. I'm only conventional on the surface to please my family, and then only as far as it suits me. I'm not going to be dictated to about anything.'

'That's what you said to that precious cousin of yours. I wish I could believe it.'

'But you can. I tell you it is so.'

'With the upbringing you've had, traditions take a lot of fighting. I know that if we're to have any more meetings you'll face a lot of opposition. We've had one example of it today. No doubt there will be others different, but equally unpleasant to you.'

'But why should there be? There is no harm in our meeting like this. My family will have to accept it.'

'Have to? Why should they? They'll fight it all the way. They hate me, they'll do everything possible to discourage you. You may think you won't be affected, but psychological pressure is a difficult thing to resist.'

'Psychological pressure! you make it sound like some kind of brainwashing.'

'Oh, nothing so refined. Just the force of family opinion.'

'I form my own opinions.'

'I hope so. And stick to them. Because if you don't, when the family bring their big guns to bear the battle will be over.'

A little cold fear was beginning to clutch at Elena's heart. She felt uncomfortable, a trifle unsure. She looked at Gregor defiantly, trying to thrust the feeling away. Now that she knew she loved him no one should stop her from doing what she wanted to do. She had put the family interests first for long enough, had been denied one man she had loved.

CHAPTER SEVEN

'Puenterojo! Puenterojo!'

Elena shook herself out of her reverie, stood up and dragged her case from the luggage rack. She would have to make her own way from here. Her mother was expecting her to arrive with Carlos by car. He had in fact telephoned her the previous evening, but with the earlier encounter of that day fresh in her mind she had curtly refused his offer and rung off. She could hardly bear to see or speak to him, she was not going to sit in a car with him hour after hour, a virtual prisoner.

It had been so hot in the train, hotter than when she had gone to Varena, although it was earlier in the day. Outside the train there would be a breeze. But when she stepped on to the platform it was like passing the open door of an oven, the breeze itself was hot. It was the hot wind from the north which everyone hated; it made one so uncomfortable and set the nerves jangling.

Her case was heavy and she was not used to carrying luggage. She set it down on the platform and looked around; there was bound to be someone who would carry it down the street for her and be glad of the tip. Out of the corner of her eye she glimpsed a tall young man in a light suit. The fair hair was unmistakable.

'I thought you might be on the train, he said. 'Let me take that.'

'How good of you to come! Did my mother — ?'

'I believe she is expecting you by car. But as I had to collect some stores I thought I would meet the train just in case you were on it.'

They were walking out of the station.

'It's only the truck, I'm afraid. Not very comfortable.'

How thoughtful of Vicente to make an excuse to meet the train. He knew she did not like Carlos.

'Oh, it's so hot!' she exclaimed.

'Yes, the Lunatics' Wind. We'll have it for a few days now. Did you enjoy your stay in Varena?'

'Very much. And I am going back on Sunday. My mother doesn't know that yet, and I don't suppose it will please her.' Nothing she intended to say would please her mother.

'Vicente,' she went on. 'I am so glad you have met me, because there is something I want to ask you. I can't wait until I get home, and you must know.'

'What is it?'

'It's about Valdoro, of course. What is being left to us? Not financially — of the *estancia*, I mean.'

'Don't you know? Your mother has been informed. The *estancia* has been so well run that you have been given the maximum allowance of land proportionate to its size.'

'But what is that? And what about the house? And *what* land? Some stock, too, I hope.'

He smiled at her eagerness, her anxiety, and told her.

'The house is yours, and the land around it. To the south, down to the river. To the north and west.'

He gave her details and distances, and she listened intently, visualizing the territory which would still belong to them.

'It's better than I'd dared to hope,' she said at last.

'You've earned it. You've been allowed so much because you've not only farmed well, you've cared for the workers and given them fair wages and good accommodation. The Government doesn't want to take all the land from people who are capable of handling it properly.'

'You are talking like General Marint!'

He laughed. 'That's not surprising. On this subject I think as he does.'

He had given her good news. It meant her plans would work, the marriage was not necessary from any viewpoint.

'About the stock, Vicente, I hope you'll give me my choice

of beasts. I know what I want.'

'I'm sure you do. I'll see if it can be arranged.'

Elena felt heartened. On the train she had felt utterly dispirited, nothing was going right. But now she had something to work on, there was really no reason why she shouldn't get her own way.

'I can't tell you how relieved I am, Vicente. Now there will be no need for Mother to threaten me with selling Valdoro!

'*Threaten*? Threaten *you*?' He gave her a horrified look. 'She couldn't do that, surely? The house has always belonged to the Mourales.'

It was not until the late afternoon that Doña Luisa had a serious talk with Elena. She had greeted her formally merely offering her cheek to be kissed, and Elena was left in no doubt that her mood had not softened since she wrote the letter demanding Elena's return; her whole manner was one of cold displeasure and disapproval. But there was nothing more than an exchange of polite enquiries and small talk until after the siesta.

'Pour me some coffee, Elena.'

They were in the small drawing-room overlooking the patio. The windows were wide open, the shutters closed, in an attempt to reduce the heat by excluding the sun. But the air that puffed through the slats was hot, they felt half-stifled.

When the Lunatics' Wind blew Doña Luisa drank small cups of black coffee almost incessantly, and kept at hand a bottle of eau de cologne and a linen handkerchief which, well sprinkled, was laid across her brows. Her largest fan, of black lace embroidered with sequins on tortoiseshell sticks, hung from her wrist when the actual effort of using it became too great.

'I am quite sure, Elena, I do not need to tell you how deeply your attitude has grieved and disappointed me.'

'You mean you are upset because I will not marry Carlos.'

'I mean I am offended because you have deliberately defied my instructions, ignored my expressed wishes.'

I am sorry, Mother.'

'I hope that you have been considering the matter carefully and have realized that I know what is best. You have wounded Carlos by your refusal. You have been wilful and thoughtless. But he loves you, so I expect that will be smoothed over. Now let us have no more delay. I want Don Pablo to have your formal acceptance so that we can announce the engagement.'

'It's no good, Mother. I can't marry Carlos.'

For a long moment Doña Luisa stared at her. 'I wish you to marry Carlos, she said at last, 'for reasons you seem incapable of grasping. Just what do you expect me to do now? You know what your alternative is. Shall I start my enquiries among the widowers? You will probably be reduced to the middle-class ones who think they have enough money to buy their way into a good family!'

Her tone was biting, scornful. Elena flushed.

'That's not fair! You know there is no need for me to marry — that's why I feel entitled to refuse someone I don't love. I could keep myself by working. But soon there will be no need for that either — if you will only let me tell you my plans.'

'You will certainly not be allowed to *work*! And what other plans could you possibly have? I suppose I had better listen to you, though if you think you have found a way to solve our problems without marrying Carlos it must be something in the realms of fantasy!'

'It's nothing of the sort, Mother. It's a perfectly practical plan for Valdoro.'

'For Valdoro?'

Doña Luisa set down her cup sharply and began to pass her fingers along her folded fan.

'Yes. We haven't lost nearly as much land as we expected, so — '

'What do you know about the land? I have told you nothing yet.'

'Vicente told me, because I asked him. I couldn't wait till I saw you.'

'You have been discussing my affairs with that shopkeeper's son! How dare you! Have you no pride?'

'He is an estate manager and knows the facts officially. Pride doesn't come into it.'

'Obviously!'

'The point is, we have some land, and some money   '

'Did you discuss my financial situation with him too?' Doña Luisa's voice was dangerously sweet.

'Of course not. But you will have been given some compensation, I know that, and I have my settlement. I am sure it will be enough.'

'Enough for what?'

Doña Luisa began to tap her fan upon her open palm as her temper and impatience began to rise.

'Enough to start a profitable business. Up to now we've raised crops, bred horses and kept cattle. With the land left to us crop-raising will be out completely. We'll cut down drastically on the working horses – we shan't need many – but keep the bloodstock at full strength. For cattle, for a start, I'll hand-pick the beasts that remain to us, and we'll fence our land completely with wire, so there will be no straying or mixing – '

'For heaven's sake, Elena!' her mother interrupted, bringing her fan down on her palm with an irritable smack. 'We are here to discuss your marriage, not to have a lecture on farm management and animal husbandry!'

'Please, Mother, I'm just getting to the whole point of it! Valdoro will still be a profitable concern for you, because we will be concentrating on high-quality stock. In the ordinary way a small *estancia* couldn't compete with the big ones in cattle rearing. But most of the cattle in Riqueza are pretty poor stock.

'We will buy a few pedigree beasts for breeding, and in a few years' time we will be able to supply breeding stock to improve the quality of other herds. They will soon want to do that when they find that better cattle bring better beef prices.'

'What a fantastic idea! You talk airily of buying pedigree

cattle, and in a few years' time selling stock, but what about money? How do we live? It's completely impractical!'

'No, Mother, it isn't. I've thought it out quite clearly. We shall have to spend quite a lot of money on a few top-quality beasts, but that will be our major outlay. I know what I'm doing. In a few years' time Valdoro cattle will be as well known as Valdoro horses for their pedigree. People will be wanting quality stock and we will be ready to supply it. In this way we will put what land we have to the best use, and the very fact that it's been reduced will be an advantage. It means that it is small enough for us to enclose it and keep our stock to ourselves. And I shall be able to supervise all of it.'

'No, Elena. I will have nothing to do with such a hare-brained scheme.'

Elena got up. How could one convince someone who was wilfully refusing to understand?

'Then let me have access to my money. With my settlement I can make a start.'

'That money was intended for your future, and I couldn't possibly allow you to throw it away like that. You must have some to take with you when you marry. No, Elena, you can stop side-tracking the discussion.'

'But this is the future I want. To look after Valdoro.'

'You are either being very obstinate or ridiculously sentimental. You have always known that as a woman you would marry and leave here. That is a woman's place in life – you can't go on aping a man.'

'I have never aped a man. And where would you be now if I hadn't taken over the running of Valdoro? You couldn't get a manager – by now the place would be run down to nothing!'

'Don't lose your temper with me, please. I don't deny that you have done well, but it was only a stop-gap, and now we must go back to a normal life. We can't go on living here like this. I did not expect to have to say such a thing, but it is your duty to me to marry Carlos. Now my circumstances are so much reduced you cannot afford to turn down such a suitable and generous offer.'

Elena stood with her back to the window, fighting to keep a cool head and to control the bitter words which were in her mind.

'Please, Mother, think it over. It's a good scheme, I can do it and it will work. Why are you so insistent that I should marry Carlos? Father would never have tried to make me —'

'Your father, God rest his soul, made a great mistake in giving way to your wilfulness and obstinacy. You should have married Carlos five years ago — and now our situation is so altered that you cannot afford to refuse!'

'I fail to see why not.'

Doña Luisa gave a sigh of extreme exasperation.

'Because your Uncle Pablo is being most generous to us.'

'What do you mean? In what way?'

Her mother did not speak at once, and Elena began to answer her own question. 'I think I see. Uncle Pablo doesn't want a dowry. That's it, isn't it?'

Her mother pressed her lips together, then inclined her head. 'That is one important point. Pablo says that he would not think of asking for a dowry when the marriage is within the family, and since you will be such a suitable wife for Carlos.'

'Suitable! Suitable! Everything is so *suitable!* Well, Carlos is not suitable to *me.* I can't even bear him to touch me. As for the dowry — it's an objectionable custom, thank God it s dying out — and from the practical angle I don't see that it makes any difference to you. If I don't marry, you won't have to give me a dowry either, and I can keep myself one way or the other. I shan't be any expense to you in the future. I'll see to that!'

'Control yourse . Elena That is no way to speak to me. It is not a question of your being an expense to me. It is a question of seeing you settled and provided for, and a matter of the future of Valdoro.'

'I've told you how to manage Valdoro! And if you won't do that, I can't see that my marrying Carlos will do the *estancia* any good!

101

'You do not know everything. I still have some control – and some personal knowledge – of my own affairs.'

'Then if my marrying Carlos has anything to do with them I have a right to know.'

'Very well, I will tell you. If you marry Carlos you will of course have to spend some time in Varena. But I am expecting to provide you both with apartments here so that you can stay as and when you wish. This will in effect be your country home. In consideration of that, your Uncle Pablo has promised me a yearly allowance towards the upkeep of Valdoro, which is going to be quite excessive as I now have no income from the *estancia*.'

Elena fumbled with the catch of the shutters and threw them open. The smell of eau de cologne in the shadowed room was overpowering. The hot air from the patio billowed in on shafts of sunlight.

She turned to her mother, clutching the shutter's edge with damp fingers, the meaning of what had just been said penetrating slowly through the layers of her consciousness.

'Uncle Pablo – is waiving the dowry – and giving you a yearly allowance – in return for the marriage? *He's buying me!* You are selling your own daughter, just as if he were some Pasha, looking about for a woman to pay money for and present to his son! It's disgusting. How could you do such a thing? I'm being bought – for Carlos de Zurga!'

'Don't be ridiculous, Elena! I never heard such mis-representation in all my life!'

'And I never heard of such an arrangment in a civilized country! How did you reckon the bride-price – on the value of so many head of cattle? I'm sorry to disappoint you, but even to help the upkeep of Valdoro I can't bring myself to agree. I'm sorry I'm such a liability to you. But it won't be for much longer. I shall leave here on Sunday, and on Monday I shall take up the post which has been offered to me in Varena. I had only been regarding it as a temporary position, to bring in a salary while matters were being settled here. But it now looks as if it will be a permanency.'

Doña Luisa stared at her coldly. 'Don't be in too much of a hurry to decide, Elena. Do you realize that, if you do not marry Carlos, I shall have to make my own arrangements concerning the future of Valdoro? You may as well know that I do not intend to stay on at Valdoro under these conditions. Therefore I shall probably make over the *estancia* to Pablo, since it will only be a trouble and expense to me.'

'*Make over* Valdoro? But I've told you I'll run it. And after all I am the next – '

'The next to inherit? But just what do you think you are entitled to from me if you continue to be so disobedient?'

'You may think, nothing! But Uncle Pablo isn't even a Moural. You can't cut out all father's family – '

'I can if I wish. I shall do as I think fit with my own property. But I will tell you this: you can have Valdoro with Carlos, or you can have neither. Since you are so insistent on having a choice, there it is.'

The room fell silent. Elena stood rock-still. Then she began to move slowly towards the door.

'Kindly close the shutters before you go. My head is aching,' were her mother's parting words.

Doña Luisa sat and fanned herself, while Elena did as she was bidden and then left the room. For a minute or two the drawing-room was still and silent except for the rhythmic swish of the fan and the glinting of its sequins in the half-dark. Then Doña Luisa rose and went to her writing desk. She sat down, drew out a sheet of paper and began writing firmly and smoothly the words she knew by heart.

'*A marriage has been arranged, and will shortly take place, between Carlos Pablo Manuel de Zurga, eldest son of Señor Don Pablo de Zurga and the late Señora Doña Esperanza de Zurga, and Elena Consuelo Maria Dolores Moural de Valdoro, daughter of the late Señor Don Fernado Moural de Valdoro . . .*'

Oh, yes, Elena would come round. She was sure of that.

CHAPTER EIGHT

Still the hot wind blew. It was not called the Lunatics' Wind for nothing. It seemed to cause as much disquiet to the nerves as it did to the body, perhaps because the wind itself contradicted nature.

One expected a wind to be cool, or at least to give some illusion of reducing temperature by the movement of air as it blew; but this wind, sweeping steadily over the land mass from the equatorial regions to the more southerly latitudes, had the opposite effect. One moved about clammy with perspiration, the lightest work brought discomfort, heavy work was a purgatory, and at the same time as it caused lassitude and lethargy the wind made tempers quick and violent and stretched nerves to breaking point.

Vicente Vargas blamed the Lunatics' Wind for his sudden mental unease. Daily his disquiet deepened, for no reason at all. Years ago he had been asked to keep a certain matter secret, and he had done so. It was no business of his, as long as he kept his word. How could he press for it to be brought into the open?

He had been brusquely banished from Elena's life, and by his own deliberate self-exile he believed he had made the separation permanent. He had been roughly dragged back, and now the hidden knowledge was disturbing him, insisting that secrecy was ill-advised, unjust; the tenuous thread was tugging at him, trying to draw him once again into her family affairs.

He had agreed to silence more readily than he might have done because he felt it might save Elena from hurt, but now perhaps this might be preferable to avoid a greater injury. Or was he under the stress of the Wind, imagining everything?

Of one thing he was sure. There was some tension between

Doña Luisa and Elena, and Elena was unhappy. He wished he knew the reason, but he could not expect her to confide in him now. From his experience Doña Luisa was a determined and unscrupulous person, and in any conflict between her and her daughter he feared Elena would come off the worse. She could match her mother in strength of will, but Doña Luisa's lack of scruple gave her extra fire-power.

Perhaps he would learn something more on Sunday. He would not see Elena until then, for he was making a final inspection and sleeping two nights on the pampa.

In any case, he would not be spending any time in the house now. With the *estancia* finally assessed, Marint had given up the use of Elena's office. A building near the bunk-house was being converted into living quarters and an office for the State Farm manager, and he, Vicente, was already living there.

On Sunday morning he would return from the pampa and, provided his successor arrived on schedule, he would go back to Varena that afternoon. Elena had agreed to travel with him. A few years ago that would have been impossible. In Varena he would spend some time at the Ministry, going on to another *estancia* as the General directed.

Back in Varena he might press to be relieved from his promise of silence, he might urge the advisability of bringing the matter into the open. Perhaps he would ask the General for advice: on consideration that seemed a sensible thing to do.

Inside the great house the Wind was taking its toll. Doña Luisa had succumbed to an attack of migraine, although for that Elena's obstinacy took most of the blame.

The servants went about their work grumbling and trying all their favourite remedies to alleviate discomfort.

Elena found it difficult to concentrate on anything in particular, but forced herself to sort out some of her possessions and to pack such things as she would need if her stay in Varena were to be prolonged.

The house was empty and silent, and in spite of its thick

walls and closed shutters, simmering with heat. She went into her own room.

'Why is everything so difficult?' she whispered. 'Why is my own mother against me?'

It was no use. She could not go on deceiving herself. Valdoro and her marriage proposal – they were only part causes of her feelings of frustration. Ever since the realization of her love for Gregor Marint had flashed upon her the emotion had been inescapable. It was part of her existence, it coloured every thought.

She wanted him so desperately. She wanted his love, but that was impossible. She told herself she could be happy with his friendship if only she could see him, talk to him, feel the stimulation of his masculinity. There was strength in every movement of his body, in the resonance of his voice, in his quick flashing glance, in the smile that puckered his eyes and creased his cheek. Just now she needed strength.

She had the horrid feeling of being caught in a web spun by Carlos and her mother. She was beginning to be enmeshed in threads of aversion and fear.

Carlos wanted to marry her, and for that reason alone she had begun to feel afraid in spite of her naturally courageous spirit. She could not understand his persistence in the face of her unwillingness; he had retired to nurse his injured pride quickly enough on the previous occasion. It was plain enough why her mother was supporting him, family loyalties and pecuniary advantage were both compelling factors. But she could not be serious in her threat about Valdoro.

The Mourales would never stand for their home being made over to a de Zurga, even though most of them now lived outside Oro Province and hadn't visited the place for years. She must call her mother's bluff, assert her independence, go back to Varena and take up her post – and seek advice from Doña Ana. And she would ring Gregor.

She lay on the bed relaxed, feeling a wave of near-happiness wash over her. A little more determination and the situation would improve. When Carlos and her mother saw that she would not give in they would have to abandon their plans.

With her eyes closed she wallowed in the reassurance of that thought. Even her physical discomfort seemed to be lessening, though it was ridiculous to think one's mental attitude could have such an effect.

Then she nearly laughed out loud – how foolish she was! The breeze had dropped. The Lunatics' Wind had nearly blown itself out. The weather was changing. There might be a storm later on, but that would have its advantages. Now it was cool enough for her to enjoy a ride.

She swung her legs off the bed and felt her energy returning to her. Soon she had changed and was in the stables chatting to Pedro while Estrella was saddled. She told him where she would be riding; her father had made a rule that solitary riders must always let their direction be known in case of accidents. Then she mounted and was away.

The air was still, the heat no longer oppressive. She would have a good long ride, it might be her last at Valdoro for a little while. Ahead lay the pampa, a glorious immensity of grass, matched only by the sweep of sky from horizon to horizon. Here there were no mean restrictions; troubles fell away, petty annoyances disappeared.

'Ay . . . o! Ay . . . o!'

She had been riding for a long time, and had seen no one. She heard the cry, faintly at first and at some distance, the call the *vaqueros* used to attract each other's attention. She reined in and looked around.

The call was repeated; it came from behind her. She turned Estrella, gazing back the way she had come, and saw a single rider moving towards her, riding fast.

She touched up Estrella and began to go back on her tracks. What did the man want? Had there been an accident? He was nearer now, and she could see he was not dressed as a *vaquero*. Was it Vicente then? Had something happened? He was not due back until the following morning.

The rider was coming at a full gallop on a powerful black

horse — surely that was Diablo? With a bound of the heart she guessed who the rider might be, and tried to still her excitement for fear she would be disappointed. But she urged Estrella into a quicker pace and raised her arm in greeting.

The man took off his sombrero and waved it, then clapped it back on his head and bent over his horse's neck. It was. It must be Gregor.

They were racing towards each other, the distance between them narrowing fast. He pulled up Diablo in a sudden flurry of dust and caracoled into position beside her as she checked Estrella. His hand went out and clasped hers, his eyes glowed down at her. Neither of them spoke.

Then their remarks came simultaneously.

'What are you doing here?'

'Pedro told me where to find you.'

They both laughed. He released her hand, but stayed for a few moments leaning towards her in the saddle, his eyes on her face as he rested easily on the high pommel. Then: 'Did you know I was at Valdoro?' she asked at last.

'I found out. When I found you had left Varena I got impatient. It was Saturday, so I borrowed a jeep and here I am!'

'You'll stay the night?'

'I hoped you'd say that!'

And now she looked fully at him, wide-eyed with happiness, not attempting to conceal her joy at his arrival.

'I wondered if you were determined to give me a drenching — you've led me quite a dance. Now we'd better turn back or we'll get wet.'

They set off in the direction of Valdoro, riding side by side, almost knee to knee.

'I wasn't bothering about the weather.'

'Nor was I. And I didn't want to wait for you at the house.'

She darted a smile at him. 'You could have ridden just a mile and ambushed me from your own territory.'

'You make me wish I had. I've never caught anything so good in an ambush before! My own territory — that's magnan-

108

imous of you!'

She looked up at the sky. 'We'll be soaked before we're home.'

The storm clouds had built up with amazing speed, now they were a flying mass of grey piled up on the horizon, beginning to sweep across the sun. The shadows were racing across the pampa.

The first lightning flash cut jaggedly across the purplish grey of the sky. Estrella whinnied with fear, Diablo shied and showed the whites of his eyes as a rending crack of thunder followed.

Then the heavens opened and the rain came down in a cold, crashing torrent. The horses were frightened and took a lot of managing. Each lightning flash turned the rain into a solid silver sheet before them, but the drops felt more like cold sharp needles of steel as they lashed against face and throat.

Marint turned and grinned at Elena.

Elena felt excited, exhilarated by the storm. Was this how men felt when they rode into battle? Battle or not, she felt she could ride with Gregor anywhere and not care about the consequences.

Pedro must have been watching and listening for them. He limped out as they clattered up and a lad darted out behind him. While Diablo was still moving Gregor swung himself out of the saddle, giving the reins to the lad. Pedro took Estrella and as Elena dismounted Gregor clasped her arm.

'Come on!' he shouted, and they raced together across the courtyard to the nearest door. When Carmela opened the door to them, she raised her arms in horror.

'*Ay, Hija!*' she wailed. 'What a state to be in! And you, General! You might both be spirits of the drowned. This rain is good, but you have had too much of it already!'

Sitting at table opposite *La Hija* in the small dining-room Gregor congratulated himself on his luck. It could hardly have turned out better.

Several times on the way to Valdoro he had cursed his folly

in letting the girl get such a hold on him that he could not stay away from her.

It wasn't just a physical desire, that would have been straightforward; he wanted her, but he could no longer deny that there was a mental or spiritual need in him of which he had been until recently hardly aware, but which now tormented him and which it seemed she might fulfil. Such complications in himself, a plain soldier, were ridiculous, but since they were there they were better dealt with as soon as possible.

When he had reached Valdoro *La Hija* had been out riding. Old Pedro told him where she had gone and began to saddle Diablo without being asked.

'*La Hija* is unhappy,' he remarked. 'Perhaps it is only the Lunatics' Wind, perhaps not. But the Wind has dropped, and you have come, so with good luck *La Hija* will be happy again.'

'Pedro, you old rogue, how can you be sure whether she is happy or sad?' he had asked jokingly.

The old man had not taken it as banter. He had straightened up, and from the seamed brown leather of his face two bright black eyes had given Marint a proud fierce stare.

'I know *La Hija*, General. Who better than I? I was here before she was born. I served her father, he was a great gentleman, and her brother — may their souls rest with God. It was I who, with Don Fernando, taught *La Hija* to ride. I have watched her grow up from a tiny baby, and I love her. With all respect I love her as I would my own daughter. Yes, General, I hope to serve her until I die. And I would kill any man who harmed one hair of her head.'

'Even me, Pedro?'

The black eyes still held his. 'Even you, General.'

'Good. It's as well we're on the same side.'

Pedro did up the last buckle.

'I am beginning to know you too, General; I have no fear for *La Hija* when you are near.'

And now, after a hot bath and a change of clothes he was having dinner alone with her. He had expressed conventional regrets on hearing that the Señora Moural was not well enough to join them, but the words meant nothing. He was delighted at the situation.

La Hija looked lovelier than ever. She was wearing a simple clinging dress of deep ivory colour, with a necklace and earrings of large topaz stones.

Her black hair, her creamy skin and soft red lips, her eyes so large and dark and brilliant, made her face even in repose a picture one could dream on. But she was a living, breathing beauty, who looked at him with wide and sparkling eyes, whose lips, having the faintest lift at each corner, were slightly tremulous. as if she was just controlling a feeling of happy anticipation.

Was he being conceited in thinking she too was glad that they were alone, that she had dressed with care with him in mind, that her hopes for the evening might be the same as his?

He wanted to start making love to her over the dinner table, but that would be bad tactics. He must not embarrass her; the servant was coming in and out with dishes and trays of food, so he must wait until they would not be interrupted. At present conversation must be on safer subjects.

'I didn't know you were coming back to Valdoro so soon.'

'Nor did I. My mother wrote and asked me to return.'

'Couldn't she cope without you? You weren't away long.'

'It wasn't that.'

'I'm not so sure. You have a way of making yourself indispensable, *Hija de Valdoro*.'

She smiled, and the faintest of blushes crept to her cheeks.

'Why don't you use my first name? I use yours now.'

'And so you should. I told you to a long time ago.'

'Then why not?'

He shrugged. 'As "Señorita Moural" sounds so very formal I prefer to use your title. To me that has a feeling of respect — and affection. You have never given me permission to call you anything else.'

111

'Permission! You don't need permission. Please, Gregor, I want you to use my first name.'

'Then that's different. I'll make up for lost time. Elena . . . Elena . . . Elena . . .'

He said her name softly and caressingly, and each time her smile deepened a little. He was reluctant to stop when it pleased them both so much. If he stretched his hand across the table he could clasp her own, but he avoided touching her even by accident. The blood was pounding in his body, the slightest contact would trigger off his desire.

At the end of the meal María served them coffee in the drawing-room. *La Hija* had ordered the best brandy for him, and allowed him to pour her a little in one of the old crystal glasses. He sat opposite her as they sipped their coffee and brandy.

The curtains were drawn over the closed and shuttered windows; outside, although the storm had dropped, the rain still fell. The silence between them was not awkward, it was the silence of two people pausing on the brink of love.

The coffee tray was taken away, the maid dismissed. He slowly drank the last of his brandy, and looked at *La Hija*.

There were no differences between them now; they were simply man and woman, irresistibly drawn to each other, inescapably involved. He set down his glass, got up and sat beside her on the couch. His eyes held hers; she waited for him to speak.

'Elena . . . *querida mia* . . . it's time. You know it's time.'

'Time for what?' she asked softly.

'Time to admit what we feel — that we must have each other.'

The intensity of his gaze made hers falter and she looked away. Very gently he took her chin in his hand and turned her face to his.

'Don't be so shy, *mi amor*,' he murmured, and put his arm round her. Bending his head he brushed her lips with his. It was the lightest, slightest contact. Her lips trembled, parted a trifle, and he began to stroke her hair.

112

Moving his head from side to side he touched her lips with his again and again, each time for a mere moment.

'*Amorcita mía*, you are so lovely.

His fingers stroke her forehead and her cheek, his lips touched hers once more. She moved and her arms crept round his neck, she turned fully to him and he knew he was accepted.

His arms tightened round her and his mouth took hers strongly and fiercely, he felt her body leap and then relax against his as she surrendered. He drew his lips away and began to trace a line of kisses down her throat, pausing at the hollow in the base of her neck, his cheek against the faintly perfumed skin.

'*Dios*, how I want you!'

He raised his head and looked deep into her eyes.

'*Elena mía*, you have no idea what you can do to me. I believe you could pull me out of the grave with your little finger.'

Her hand pressed lightly on his lips. 'Hush! Don't tempt Providence.'

'Providence!' he laughed. 'It's you I want to tempt.'

He kissed her again. Soon they would lie together naked, by moon- or candle-light, and he would adore her loveliness with caressing fingers and yearning mouth. His need for her was almost overmastering him. He raised his head to speak — was that his voice, thick with emotion? How it betrayed him!

'*Amorcita mía*, let us go to your room.'

She had taken such a hold over his mind and feelings; he had no doubt that sooner or later there would be consummation, so delay was unreasonable, pointless. But she gave no answering word or nod, and he looked at her, to find her eyes questioning and uncertain.

'Don't be afraid of me, sweetheart. I'm not an ignorant schoolboy. I won't be rough or clumsy with you. I will see that your enjoyment is no less than mine. Trust me.'

He unclasped her necklace and put it aside. 'It's in my way,' he murmured. 'I'll make you one of kisses.'

113

He ran his fingers lightly down her throat, then held her bare shoulders as his lips traced where the necklace had lain.

'It needs a pendant.'

His warm mouth began to move downwards, but she caught his head in her hands.

'Gregor, you are asking me to . . .'

'I'm not asking you anything. You have told me. Not in words but in kisses, that you are ready to belong to me. There couldn't be a better time -- now, when we need each other, and we have the night before us.'

His face bent over hers, he saw her lips tremble before she spoke.

'Not now, Gregor. Not now.'

'Trust me, *querida*. It shall be exactly as you say. Now let us go to your room. I can't wait to make love to you as I want to and as you deserve.'

She shook her head, her wide eyes pleading. Didn't she want him after all?

'No, Gregor, we can't. You know that.'

'I don't know it. I know we must. What's stopping us?'

'Must I say it? How can we? We are not married . . .'

At any other time it would have been laughable. She looked and sounded so innocent, so naïve, like a girl of fourteen, not a woman of twenty-four.

But how could she talk like that, after the admission she had made to him months ago? And why should she put him off in such a childish, trifling way? He had not thought himself a jealous man, but now knowledge was burning within him, rising up, making his face flame, searing his throat and choking him.

He stared down at her, silently fighting for control, and she looked up at him, actually surprised at his expression. The words ground out of him.

'And is my love, then, so much less than his?'

It made it worse that he had guessed who the man was. This way it was something definite, he couldn't ignore it. God, it was worse than a bullet wound. And that word he had sworn

114

never to use again had been forced out of him it was the only one that fitted after all. Love — yes, he loved her, more fool he!

'What do you mean? I don't understand — '

'But I do. You told me you had had a lover. I'm no gentleman to mention it, but there, I'm just a brigand, aren't I? You had no scruples about marriage then, so what is it? What makes me so different? Was he such a noble character? Does that make sinning easier?'

He could not watch her seeking for words. He let her go and stood up abruptly, then began to walk to and fro, trying not to look at her.

'You thought *that*? You asked me what happened to my lover, and I told you. But I didn't mean . . . We were deeply in love, but we were not lovers in that sense. How could you have thought it possible?'

He felt the blood drumming in his head. Had she been playing with him, then? Didn't she mean to give herself — ever? Was it true she had never belonged to a man?

Yes, it was true, he felt it, it explained a lot. And yet it was absurdly little comfort to him.

'Why shouldn't it be possible? I'm not suggesting you behaved like a prostitute. Plenty of women — moral women — gave themselves in time of war, gave themselves with love, sharing a happiness in case they never had a marriage. I was prepared for that with you. I wasn't prepared to be played with.'

'*Played with*?'

'Isn't that what you've been doing? You responded to me so completely, and all the time — all the time you were banking on your judgment of me. You're right, of course. I have my faults, plenty of them, but I draw the line at seducing virgins.'

In his anger he was pleased to see he had shocked her.

'I'm just a common soldier, but I don't rape them either, even when they've asked for it. You're quite safe.'

He wanted to sting her into a reply, to make her give him a

fight so that he could work off his rage and then smooth over the misunderstanding, but she sat there speechless.

He turned and began to pace the room, not looking where he was going; his elbow caught a sheaf of papers on the little writing desk and they showered to the floor. He swore under his breath and bent to pick them up. What an idiot he had been, ever to think she could have gone outside the bounds of convention imposed by her class! He might as well have believed she would dance naked in front of the *vaqueros*. It would be just as possible. Of course she would keep herself untouched until she married. Virginity was essential.

He was on his knees gathering the scattered papers into his hand. On one he saw her name, and without conscious intention he had in one long glance taken in the whole meaning of what was written there.

He stood up, thrusting the sheaf of papers back on to the desk, except for one which he held, willing himself not to crumple it into a ball, forcing his hand to be steady.

'I hope you have enjoyed yourself this evening.'

His voice was harsh, loaded with sarcasm. Still she did not answer.

'Well, haven't you? Weren't you amused to see just how far I wanted to go? Quite a triumph for you, wasn't it, when all the time your marriage is settled? Were you having your last fling, a risky little flirtation before you're one man's property? Were you going to throw this in my face at the end of the evening, or wasn't I supposed to see it?'

He thrust the paper in front of her, the paper which bore her name and Carlos de Zurga's, the announcement in Señora Moural's elegant handwriting of her daughter's forthcoming marriage.

Elena actually managed to look as if she was seeing it for the first time.

'Gregor, did you think — '

No wonder she was uncertain what to say.

'What am I to think? I'll tell you! I thought you were a real woman, with courage to acknowledge your emotions. But now

116

I see you're as hidebound as all your class, and as fearful of stepping out of line. Unfortunately I'm not a man who feels no passion until he's been mumbled over by a priest. So I shock you with my honest desires and plain speaking. But you shock me, when you're prepared to marry a decadent, inbred. vicious little bastard like de Zurga simply because he's got the right name and comes here waving a marriage contract.'

'It isn't true, Gregor! I haven't agreed. That was written without my knowledge.'

'I've believed everything else, but I can't believe that. Why else should you be here? Why should your mother write this if it isn't practically settled? Didn't she send for you to tell you so? At least I hope you won't insult my intelligence by pretending to be in love with that gutless little boudoir-jumper!'

Her eyes flashed at him proudly. 'I'm not in love with him! You seem to think you have the right to be angry, but that is no reason for throwing your barrack-room language at me.'

'Oh, I beg your pardon!' he retorted ironically. 'I'm not used to fancy phrases. So you don't think I have the right to be angry? I only lost my head over you, so my feelings don't count. I can stay dangling on my string while you're seriously considering the fellow who keeps a tame lawyer handy ready to settle the practical details. I suppose I should have sent in a bid in writing. Long live the noble old institution of the marriage market!'

'That has nothing to do with it!'

Now she was angry, and he couldn't bear that either.

'It has everything to do with it. It certainly has for your mother, and she's the law around here, isn't she? Does she keep you posted about the bargaining? Isn't that why you rushed back? Did de Zurga make a better offer — one too good to refuse?'

'How dare you speak to me like that!'

'How dare I? I speak as I think fit, whether it's to the President or a *peón*, so don't think I'll mince my words for a Moural, even if you do think yourselves next to God!'

117

He crumpled up the paper in his fingers, crushed it into a tight ball and threw it on the floor in front of her. It was a theatrical gesture, but it expressed his feelings.

He turned to stride out of the room, paused, then threw his last remarks at her as she sat pale and still, staring proudly at him.

'Don't bother to tell me when de Zurga pays up and signs for possession. Such a delightful custom. Take my advice — push the price up while you can. Such men are mean to their wives, having bought them! I can't help wondering how much he's prepared to give — cash down — for the legal enjoyment of your body!'

He closed the door behind him, and found his palms were sweating, his mouth dry with disgust.

Five minutes later he was in the jeep, its headlights cutting a swathe in the darkness, the beams filled with silver streaks of rain. Through the archway of the court, on to the drive, sweeping through the tall wrought-iron gates; and then he was careering crazily along the Puenterojo road. He was driving too fast, he knew it, and didn't care.

If he had stayed under the same roof with Elena there would have been trouble. In his present mood he'd either take her or break her before the night was out. He was safer driving too fast, lurching and bucketing along the road which would take him away from her, back to Varena.

CHAPTER NINE

As soon as Vicente saw Elena he knew something was wrong. But the *estancia's* mechanic who was to return with the truck to Valdoro was already sitting in the back where he would overhear everything that was said, so that Vicente knew he must be absolutely formal until they reached Puenterojo.

He handed Elena into the front passenger seat, saw her cases – more than she had brought, he noticed – into the back, and took his seat behind the wheel.

Polite conversation shuttled rather painfully back and forth. She was finding it difficult to keep her mind on what was being said. He had seen acute distress in her eyes – what was that bitch of a mother doing to her now? It needed all his diplomacy to produce just enough conversation of the right type to prevent the man in the back from suspecting they had anything more than a business relationship or from guessing there was anything amiss. It seemed a very long drive to Puenterojo.

At last they were alone in a first class compartment, and he turned anxiously to her. 'What's the matter, Elena? What has happened?'

Her reply came slowly. 'I've quarrelled with my mother.'

'Was it serious? May I know what it was about? Was it Valdoro?'

Again the slow reply, as if she were almost in a trance. 'Yes. Yes, about Valdoro.'

He waited for some elucidation but none came.

'If there is anything I can do, please tell me.'

'Thank you, Vicente. But no one can do anything. My mother is determined not to keep Valdoro.'

'Not to keep – ! But you thought you could arrange

119

everything.'

'I thought so.'

Now she sounded bitter. 'I have a perfectly good plan for running the *estancia*, but my mother will not agree. So I suppose she will do as she says and make it over to Uncle Pablo.'

'She can't do that!'

The words were out before he had considered them.

'She thinks she can. If there's no written entail on the estate — perhaps that's what she intends to find out — perhaps she already knows. She saw Señor Castellán recently.'

'But it's monstrous! She must know how it would hurt you!'

'She knows. But I can't make her change her mind, so let's not talk about it. I shall have to see if Aunt Ana has any ideas.'

He could not draw Elena to tell him any more.

If Señora Moural really intended to relinquish control of the *estancia*, something would have to be done. And it looked as if he would have to make the first move. It was a damnable situation to be in. He foresaw discussions, persuasions, explanations — it would be a lengthy and harrowing business, and he must start it as soon as possible.

If there seemed the faintest chance of success he would bring the General into it. Marint was a big gun who might fire the deciding shot. But he could not tell Elena. Later on, someone would have to — not himself, if he could help it, in spite of his responsibility.

How Doña Ana fussed over her niece! She even went down to the kitchen and herself made a pot of her own special tea, which would refresh and soothe Elena better than coffee, she said. While Elena drank it the story came out. Doña Ana was aghast. How could Luisa think of giving up Valdoro? She had no right to do it — it was Moural property. It was grossly unfair not to give Elena the chance of continuing to run it since she had done so well.

'We must keep Valdoro for the Mourales!' she said decisively. 'It has always been understood that the house and

120

estancia pass to the next of kin. I shall go to see Señor Castellán as soon as possible, and ask if that is a legal fact. If it is not in writing, and Luisa chooses to ignore her moral responsibilities, something else must be done.' Her eyes were bright with indignation.

'But what can we do, Aunt?' asked Elena.

'Don't worry, darling. I have a plan already. I shall write to all the close relatives and ask them to join a sort of syndicate, for each of them to put up a sum of money to buy Valdoro from Luisa. I don't suppose any of them will want or be able to buy it outright, they've all been hit pretty hard by sequestration and taxes on capital, so they're unlikely to have that much money to spare. But if each put up a certain sum, we could buy it between us.'

Elena's face broke into a smile. 'That's a wonderful idea!'

Doña Ana began to warm to her subject. 'It gets better as it goes along! You could be in charge, running your new scheme there, with the right to buy the others out when you have the money!'

'If only they would agree. Do you think there's a chance?'

'Of course. You know our side of the family — most of them would do a lot to prevent the de Zurgas taking over their old home. Between ourselves, I think a lot of them resent Luisa even though she is a Moural by marriage.'

The staff of the Varena branch of Agricultural Chemicals Incorporated were intrigued by their new recruit. It was plain that Señorita Moural wished to be incognito; they respected her desire but congratulated themselves on discovering her identity so quickly.

The manager, who successfully combined North American business ways with Riquezan charm from his mixed parentage (which his baptismal name of Roberto Kelly proclaimed) was thankful at last to find someone whose qualifications were so close to what he required in a secretary. He didn't care whose daughter she was.

But Señor Kelly had suspected from the beginning that she

was some connection of the late Conde de Valdoro. At the interview he had remarked, most tactfully, on her total lack of references, for her application stated that she had been working in the office of a large *estancia*. She had answered him with little sign of embarrassment.

'I was working for a relation. I could hardly expect you to attach any significance to a reference signed by someone of the same name.'

There were Mourales in various parts of the country, all aristocratic, all related, and no doubt all being sequestered left right and centre, and feeling the pinch. She was one of them, and it was a fair bet that she came from Valdoro, most of which, it was public knowledge, was now a State Farm.

He tried to be sorry that she had fallen on hard times. The fact remained that secretaries with her education were rarer than gold nuggets. Valdoro's loss was his gain.

For a start, she spoke — beside her native Spanish — French, Portuguese and English, the latter as well as he did himself. She could type, she was no stranger to office work, and she had a good working knowledge of most of his firm's products. She promised to be a treasure, and he waved aside the admission that her shorthand was rusty as being a matter of little importance.

Controlling a Latin-American branch of a North American firm had its frustrations, it would be a relief to feel that he could leave the office from time to time and know that telephone calls in English would be dealt with efficiently.

The book-keeper, Señor Gomez, had some reservations about the appointment. It was certainly a blow for democracy for a young lady of her social position to take a secretarial post.

But Rosa Santos, on the other hand, was wild with excitement and curiosity. Rosa was seventeen and had grown up with the Revolution. Under the old régime, as a child of poor parents, she would have been lucky to have become an ill-paid shop assistant, but democracy had made evening classes available, opened professions to women and preached 'emancipation, so that she was now a typist, with good pay and prospects. To think that when she was small the height of her ambition had been to sell stockings and gloves in a smart shop on the Via Colón!

With the facility of youth Rosa combined a professed contempt for titles, wealth and social position with an interest in their possessors, and even a back-handed admiration for some of the idle rich, particularly if they were male and sufficiently handsome and dashing.

But the idol of Rosa's heart was, appropriately enough, no indolent aristocrat but a vigorous Revolutionary. Her serious admiration was all reserved for General Marint. In a large chocolate box kept in the chest of drawers in her bedroom she hoarded newspaper cuttings with all the flattering references to the General, and every photograph of him she came across. But the Señorita Moural actually knew him!

For Rosa's brain with burglar-alarm sensitivity had registered Elena's name with a ringing of bells. A quick reference to a newspaper cutting from the *Noticia* with its accompanying photograph was enough to prove that her memory had not played her false. Elena's rank and position paled into insignificance beside the fact that she had not only met and talked to General Marint but had been singled out by him to be his partner in a visit to the Opera. That meant that she must know him very well.

Of course she was in love with him. No woman worth her salt could be in the company of such a man and not fall in love with him within the space of two minutes. Was he in love with her? Could he love an hidalga?

To Elena entering Agricultural Chemicals was like stepping into a new world. She was glad it was a small office; in a large one she would have felt completely lost, and here there were fewer toes to tread on, however inadvertently. Even here there was a hierarchy, she discovered, which must be observed.

As secretary to the manager she was above the typist and in a position of uneasy equality with the book-keeper. So much tact seemed to be necessary. Continually she had to remind herself that she was not expected to make decisions at this stage of her experience, efficiency and obedience were all that was required, and she must avoid any assumption of authority in act or in manner. It was not easy.

Nothing was easy nowadays. Once life had been orderly, confortable and happy; now after an uncertain period of transition she was having to fight for everything.

She had thought that all she would have to do was to give a firm refusal to Carlos and then life would settle down to its old ways. But that had not happened. Life went on changing. She was battling from day to day, with everything she loved slipping from her grasp.

It was as well that she was busy at the office. There Valdoro, the Mourales, the de Zurga marriage, all were irrelevant and meaningless and she gave all her mind to her work.

After a few days she admitted to herself that it was harder than she had expected. The hours, from eight to noon, three to six-thirty, were much the same as she had imposed on herself at Valdoro, but the other differences were enormous.

She was used to doing her office work by herself, at her own speed and in her own way, in an atmosphere of peace and quiet. Here there were continual interruptions, telephones ringing, summonses to Señor Kelly's private office, and all the time just outside the window was the noise and smell of the city. The racket never stopped.

She was used to riding for miles in open country every day. Here her exercise consisted of walking between her desk in the outer office and Señor Kelly's desk in the inner one. A few months of this and she would be fat, flabby and unhealthy. She must consider Doña Ana's suggestion of hiring a horse on Saturdays and Sundays, even a canter in the park would be something. She was trying to live on her salary, but she couldn't let herself relapse into complete decrepitude!

Surely it wouldn't be for long? In a week or so Aunt Ana would have enough replies to her letters to know what could be done. She had written to all their close relatives to form a kind of syndicate, for each of them to put up a sum of money to buy Valdoro. The family couldn't let Valdoro go. In a few months she would be back there, caring for her horses, carrying on the stud and planning the cattle-breeding. Thank heaven, Pedro could be trusted with the horses for the time being. And if the Mourales couldn't – or wouldn't – find the money? Then she would go on working in Varena, petition for her money, and when she got it (as she must) she would buy a small place and start her scheme there, with just a few of her horses to begin with. If she hadn't quarrelled with Gregor he would have given her advice, even help – but she could manage without it, if it came to that.

What an utter fool she had been! It had been her fault the quarrel had started. She had been incredibly clumsy in her handling of the situation. For a little while everything had been so wonderful between them, but if he only wanted her for sex it was as well for her to find it out and finish with him.

But was that all? She knew now where she had made her mistake. Any peasant girl would have had the sense to hold him off and yet show at the same time that she loved him. But she had been so juvenile in her simplicity, so taken by surprise, that all she could do was to babble of marriage. Enough to put any man off, whatever his intentions. And then things had gone from bad to worse, with no chance for explanations.

The bus was crowded, and Elena had to stand most of the way. She was tired, not only from her day's work, but with an extra nervous exhaustion. She was glad when she reached her stop and got out to walk the rest of the way to the Avenida de Mayo.

As she entered the hall Doña Ana came out to meet her. With one look at her face her aunt drew her into the sitting-room. 'So you've seen it? Sit down, dearest.'

'Seen it! There was a placard on the hoarding of the building site by the office. It hit me in the eye. All my horses . . . but how did you know? Have you been into town?'

'There was an advertisement in today's paper. You haven't

seen the paper, then?'

'No. Where is it?'

Doña Ana hurriedly folded the paper to an inner page where there was a large notification.

SALE BY AUCTION

at

VALDORO

of highest quality BLOODSTOCK

from the MOURAL DE VALDORO stables. . . .

'Look at the figure it gives — she's selling every one, the whole stud. And she lets me find out this way. Look at it: "A magnificent black stallion of seventeen hands" — that's Diablo. "An unusual riding mare of perfect training and disposition" — that's Estrella. The pinto is Solysombra, and that chestnut, Paquito. All my favourites. There was no need to mention Estrella on the notice, mares are still not very popular for riding, but this is for my benefit. I'm not to be left in any doubt. Mother's seling the lot.'

Doña Ana laid a hand on her arm. 'It couldn't be intentional. The auctioneers — '

'Of course it's intentional! You can't soften the blow, you know Mother better than that. She'd like me to go to her cap in hand and say, "Please don't sell my horses, I'll marry Carlos,' so that she could consider it, and then in a lofty way withdraw a few from the auction as a sign of great forgiveness.'

Doña Ana could not deny this. She made sympathetic clucking noises, and Elena went on. 'The ironic part of it is, that if it hadn't been for me she wouldn't have a stud to sell.'

'Now, darling, don't be too upset. The auction is a week away. In that time we can do something.'

'But we can't. I won't marry Carlos, and I can't lay hands on my money, so there's nothing we can do.'

'Oh, yes, there is.'

She turned swiftly to face her aunt. 'No, Aunt Ana, I won't have it! You can't buy any of them back for me. You simply cannot afford it. You're subsidizing me here as it is. Have you any idea the sort of figures these horses will fetch? The country is starved of bloodstock because of the Revolution, and this will be the biggest sale for years. With our reputation everyone will be there, and each extra bidder will push the prices higher. I refuse to let you make that sort of sacrifice.'

'But I want to buy one, at least.'

'But *I* don't want you to. Oh, Aunt, think of my pride -- how wounded it would be! And I've so little left I can't afford to have it hurt.' she said wryly.

'Very well, darling, if you insist. Then I shall try to think of something else. We have a week.'

Why, oh why, thought Doña Ana rebelliously, did her brother Fernando have to die when he did? He would never have let this happen. She had known her brother so well, perhaps better than his own wife had done; she had never been blind to his faults, nor had she let death turn him into a saint in her eyes. No, he had not been perfect, but he would never have been deliberately cruel to his own daughter.

Fernando had not pressed the de Zurga marriage when it had first been proposed; had time made it more attractive in his eyes he would still have considered Elena's wishes. As for turning the girl from home and selling all her beloved horses simply because she continued to refuse it, such action would have been unthinkable.

Certainly he had considered Vicente Vargas quite impossible, and had not given an inch from the stand he took, but he hadn't victimized Elena for being in love. No doubt he would have disapproved equally violently of Gregor Marint, but if the affair had reached a similar stage he would have given her a hearing as he had done before. But Luisa's behaviour was monstrous.

Poor Elena, thought Doña Ana. She was breaking her heart over the General, though doing her best to conceal it. She had admitted to Doña Ana that they had quarrelled, but had given no indication of the cause. It must have been something radical, since neither had made any attempt to mend the rift.

Doña Ana reluctantly conceded there was nothing she could do about that. She had thought Gregor Marint really cared for Elena, but she might have been wrong. Men could be so incalculable. But Elena cared. In other circumstances Elena might have had comfort from religion; that nice priest at Puenterojo would have given her support, but here she would get precious little out of Father Xavier. He would probably tell her she was being punished for her disobedience. So she was, but not by God. By Luisa, who was behaving outrageously. One always came back to Luisa.

Very well, she thought, there's nothing else for it. I'll have to humble myself and appeal to Luisa's better nature, if she has any. Or her logic. Surely she must see that she won't get Elena's co-operation by using the sale of the horses as a bludgeon to beat her with. Not that Elena will take Carlos in any case, so what was the point? It was just vindictiveness.

With no very clear idea of what she would say, Doña Ana went to the telephone. Elena was at the office for the morning only, as it was Saturday; if she was going to talk to Luisa it would be better done in Elena's absence. Don Pablo de Zurga answered her; somehow she had not expected him to be at home. Only after she had enquired about his health and participated in the formal exchange of compliments could she get down to business.

'Is Luisa there, Pablo?'

'No, Ana, she's at Valdoro for a few days. She'll be staying until after the bloodstock sale.'

What a nuisance it was. What could she say to Pablo?

'I wanted to talk to her about the horses. Do you realize that she is selling the lot, including the ones Elena is most fond of, the ones she rides all the time?'

'Is she? I didn't know. She did say that she and Elena have had a tiff over Valdoro.'

A tiff! Was that Luisa's version? She turned her own daughter out of the house, virtually disowned her, and called it a tiff! And what about the marriage proposal? Doña Ana was floored for a moment. Did Pablo not know it was off?

128

'Luisa is being very high-handed and most unkind to Elena.'

'Well, Ana, I don't want to offend either of you. But I can see her point of view over Valdoro. After all, what is the use of the place with the few hundred acres that are left? Elena thinks she can do something with it, some fantastic idea about breeding pedigree cattle. But how can she? She won't have much time to spend there when she's married, she'll be living here with a husband and family to look after. Luisa did talk of making the *estancia* over to me, so that it would come to Carlos and Elena, but that would cause ill-feeling in the family, as you well know. No, it's no use being sentimental. I agree with her that the best thing is to put the *estancia* up for sale on the open market.'

Doña Ana listened to this long speech delivered in Don Pablo's deep deliberate tones with rising impatience and anger. It was all very well for him. He wasn't a Moural. He hadn't been born and bred at Valdoro, any more than Luisa had. It seemed that, to them, selling Valdoro was on a par with getting rid of an old coat. She checked the impulse to argue on these lines. It would be a waste of breath, especially as Pablo was under the impression that the marriage was going to take place. Luisa must have deliberately deceived him, but it would not be diplomatic of her to disillusion him. He would have to find out for himself.

'I don't want to talk about Valdoro. But the horses — surely there's no need for Luisa to deprive Elena of every single one.'

'I agree. That does seem rather drastic. But no doubt she has her reasons. She must know that Carlos will provide Elena with anything she wants, and there are plenty of horses in Mauel's care. She can have her pick when she's married.'

Doña Ana gritted her teeth. *She's not going to marry Carlos*, she wanted to shout into the telephone. She tried again.

'It's not the same, Pablo. She's particularly fond of her own horses. She's put years of work into the stud, they are something special to her, each one is a different individual.'

'But they're still just horses, Ana. Get her married and she won't have time to sentimentalize over them. She's a young woman, a husband and babies are what she needs — she should have been married years ago and so should Carlos. They'll be good for each other. She'll steady him and he'll satisfy her. When she has a man of her own she'll see things in a better proportion.'

Doña Ana felt slightly sick. So sexual relations with Carlos were supposed to work as a psychological nostrum! How disgusting middle-aged men could be!

'That's a matter of opinion, Pablo. Be that as it may, Luisa has no right to sell Elena's favourite horses without even consulting her. The first thing Elena knew about it was when she saw a poster advertising the sale on a public hoarding. That was a cruel way of doing it.'

Well, you know what Luisa's like when she's crossed. Now, if Elena were to tell her she's sorry — '

'Elena has nothing to be sorry about, Pablo. It's a difference of opinion, and Luisa is being unreasonable, though I wouldn't provoke her at this stage by saying so to her face. I wanted to ask her whether she could see her way clear to withdraw one or two of Elena's favourites from the blood-stock sale. It would go a long way towards making a reconciliation possible.'

'Reconciliation! You make it sound as though they're at daggers drawn. Still, this silly tiff is holding up the wedding plans, we haven't even made a formal announcement yet. I don't mind telling you, Ana, I'm getting impatient. I've done my bit, I've told Luisa exactly what I'm prepared to do, financially and otherwise. She has it in writing and she's perfectly satisfied. So is Carlos. Now it's up to her to get things moving. Luisa has been delayed by all the business over Valdoro, I can understand that, but it's time she and Elena settled their minor differences and dealt with the more important matter. I'm fond of Elena, and I want to see her married to Carlos. All this shilly-shallying about Valdoro and the horses! Let's forget about it and press on with the marriage arrangements, that's what I say.'

Don Pablo was growling away; Doña Ana could sense his impatience and irritation coming nearer to the surface every moment. He didn't doubt that Elena had given her consent. It was an awkward situation.

'And what does Carlos say?'

'He's impatient, naturally, but he's taking it very well – too well, I think. He's going to see Luisa next week, before the sale, and he expects everything to be smoothed over by then. These modern boys – they haven't got fire in their bellies like we had. In his position I'd have been on the doorstep every evening, ready to take the girl by storm. I know he wants her, but has he convinced *her* of it, I wonder?'

That was the last thing Doña Ana wanted to discuss. She clutched at his previous remark.

'You say Carlos is going to see Luisa?'

'Yes. Do you want him to take a message for you?'

'Now I wonder what would be best ... ' she murmured, giving Don Pablo time to think. 'If I post a letter to Luisa it may wait for collection at Puenterojo for a week or more. Then it would be too late. Do you think Carlos would be willing to put in a word about the horses?'

'I should think so.'

She could hear him warming to the idea.

'There's no need for him to mention me. Luisa might take to the idea better if she thinks it comes from him. If she could be persuaded to withdraw Estrella and Diablo and one or two of the others.'

'He could try. If he could bring it off it would make matters easier. It wouldn't do him any harm with Elena either. A little extra warmth is always welcome in a sweetheart, eh?'

Heaven forgive me, thought Doña Ana, for letting him deceive himself. It's for Elena's sake.

'I'll leave it to you, then, Pablo. I shan't say anything to Elena about it, we'll just wait and see what Carlos can do.'

From the early hours of the morning on the day of the auction,

131

the road between Puenterojo and Valdoro, usually deserted, had been thronged with people. The horse was a ruling passion in Riquezan society, and everyone, regardless of status, age or sex, shared in the fervour. It was not surprising, therefore, that a bloodstock sale of such a size from a stable with so noble a reputation should attract a great number of persons.

Everyone who could go to Valdoro, went. For most people the event was in the nature of a cross between a pilgrimage and a fair. They had no thought of buying; they went to pay reverence to a collection of splendid animals, and to enjoy a grand day's outing.

The poorest came first. Travelling on foot, carrying a day's supply of food and drink they trudged for miles, in pairs, in groups, sometimes in whole family parties. Next came folk on horse- and mule-back, the thudding hooves beginning to stir up the dust from ground already baked dry after the previous evening's rain.

Last of all, came the prospective buyers in a steadily increasing stream of Cadillacs, Lincolns, Buicks and Ferraris, with the occasional Rolls Royce favoured by the old-style landed aristocracy.

The greater part of the auction would take place in the morning; after a break for alfresco luncheons the sale would be concluded in plenty of time for folk to be well on their way home before the rain expected at this time of year in the early evening began to fall.

In the enclosure were the unmistakable Spanish features, the Latin carriage and gesture; expensive clothes and jewels, every air of refinement and luxury. Neither class apparently found any incongruity in the presence of the other.

The poor folk outside the enclosure accepted the rich folk within, and took their own exclusion as a matter of course. The hidalgos did not so much accept the lower orders as ignore them.

Everyone in the enclosure knew Doña Luisa de Zurga Moural de Valdoro by reputation, many were personally acquainted with her. Not one of them even considered going

132

to the great house in search of her. It would have been in very bad taste. To call on her at such a time would be to stress her misfortune; if they were to help her by providing ready cash in exchange for her horseflesh it must be done in an atmosphere of decent anonymity.

Doña Luisa, in her turn, was relying on their correctness. Had she chosen to entertain one person she would in courtesy be bound to invite fifty, and her staff was so depleted that what they would once have taken in their stride was now an impossibility. She hadn't enough maids even to serve wine and biscuits to such a crowd.

With Elena to organize matters and mix with the guests she might just have managed that much, but as it was, far better to pretend she wasn't even on the premises. It was lucky she had no desire to be present at the sale. She appreciated a good horse, particularly if it belonged to her, but the disposal of her whole stud was too much, and the fluctuations of bidding would have too personal a significance, although purely monetary, for her.

Gregor Marint's interest in the bloodstock sale was at first purely academic. He had seen the horses; it would be interesting to watch them in the ring and find out what prices they reached. Yes, he'd go if he could find the time.

So Elena Moural was selling all her horses. She was marrying young Moneybags, and it wouldn't be convenient to continue running the stud when she was living in Varena, that was the obvious reason.

He tried to accept the explanation, but at the back of his mind was a feeling of unease, as if something didn't fit — just as he had felt over their quarrel.

He re-read the placards and the advertisements; it was plain enough. All the horses were to go, even her favourite mount Estrella.

Sudden realization flooded over him — that was what was wrong. Why advertise Estrella out of so many? A riding mare, even of such excellence, was of no great sales interest compared with other horses in the stud which were un-specified. And why sell her at all? It wasn't like Elena. He would have said, knowing her, that she might — regretfully — sell the stud on her marriage, but she would at all costs keep Estrella for her own use, and a few more besides if possible. It certainly wasn't because de Zurga couldn't afford to maintain a few extra horses for his wife.

Perhaps she wasn't marrying him, and needed the money? No, in that case she might reduce the stud, but it wouldn't make sense to sell them all unless she was leaving Valdoro. Even then, not Estrella, surely.

What a fool he was! He'd made a wrong assumption from the start. The stud had not come under assessment, and he had always looked on it as belonging to Elena. But suppose it was owned by that tartar of a mother? It would be like her to decide to give it up, to make a clean sweep of the lot. But what a mother, to sell all Elena's mounts — how that stuck in his craw! It was a fine reward for taking the husband that had been chosen for her.

The mere thought of Elena giving herself to de Zurga caused revulsion to turn his stomach. He felt disgusted by the whole business. They were a peculiar lot. Even Elena — he hadn't expected her to give in so easily. He couldn't believe she had any affection for that lecherous little opportunist. Even in their quarrel over the marriage announcement she hadn't pretended to that.

Suddenly he saw and heard her. 'That was written without my knowledge!' And he in his rage had not believed her.

But if it had been true? Hope surged. *Dios*, what was he hoping for? How could she make such a boy of him? She was only a woman he had wanted and not taken.

No, that wasn't true. There was something about her that chimed in harmony with his deepest thoughts and beliefs so that the very fibre of his being called to her, not only for physical possession but for a union of understanding and spirit.

He had never thought any woman could affect him like

134

that, and he was still unwilling to admit it. And where was it getting him? Nowhere. He was farther away from her than ever.

But there was no reason why he shouldn't go to the bloodstock sale and make his own observations. She would be there.

By mid-day it was plain that the Valdoro horses were hitting record prices. Throughout the morning excitement had been mounting in waves around the ring with each successive sale. In spite of civil war, sequestration and taxation, there was still plenty of money about in some quarters. The best-known agents were there in force, and it was anyone's guess who they represented — the Police or the Army, perhaps, they rarely missed a sale — alternatively some big organizations or foreign millionaires preferring anonymity.

It was noticed·that General Marint was present, but in a private capacity and as an onlooker: he was out of uniform and had not made a single bid.

The auction was well advanced by the time Gregor Marint forced himself to accept that Elena would not appear. Did she consider it undignified to be present when her own horses were up for sale? Or was it not to her taste? Perhaps she had not agreed to the auction? Or was she merely waiting in the house to be told the result? He didn't know enough about the situation.

He was still turning such thoughts over in his mind as he drove in his jeep to the State Farm buildings a couple of miles away. The manager was out on the farm, so Marint and Vicente Vargas, who had accompanied him, took possession of the office.

'Vargas,' Marint said at length, 'did you expect Señorita Moural to be present at the auction?'

Vargas was taken by surprise. 'No, sir. I think not.'

'Why not? Wouldn't it be "correct"?'

'Possibly not, sir. But I didn't expect her, largely because I think the sale was being held against her wishes.'

'The devil you do! What makes you think that?'

Vicente looked embarrassed and did not answer.

'Come on, man. It's no secret that you've had some acquaintance with the family. *La Hija* herself told me you were at university with her brother. I'm not asking out of idle curiosity. Now why should you think she didn't approve of the sale? And has she no rights over the horses to prevent it?'

'The horses belong entirely to the Condesa,' Vargas said slowly. Neither man appeared to notice his slip of the tongue in using her old title. 'I think the sale was her idea. She and – and the Señorita – cannot agree over the future of Valdoro.'

'I see. So the mother goes her own way and sells the stud the daughter has put her heart into. Even sells her favourite riding horses.'

He called Doña Luisa something uncomplimentary under his breath, and noticed that Vicente, though probably in complete agreement, thought it wise to pretend not to hear.

'Didn't *La Hija* do anything about it?'

'I don't know, sir. Perhaps there was nothing she could do.'

Marint sat puffing at his cigarette and digesting the remark. 'She can't be penniless.'

'I believe the money left to her by her father cannot be touched without her mother's permission until she reaches thirty years of age. Or marries.'

So there was a reason for getting married – financial independence, of a sort. She couldn't wait six years – or maybe much less if a likeable man offered. She preferred to give herself at once. Sell herself to de Zurga. Nevertheless she was marrying the man her mother had chosen, so why should the old devil get rid of *all* the horses, even Estrella? It was singularly disobliging of her, and it still didn't fit.

But he couldn't ask Vargas any more questions without betraying his interest.

'Are you in a hurry to get back to Varena?'

'Not particularly, sir.'

'Good. I've got to go over to the house on some other

136

business, but I expect Señora Moural will be tied up with her agent for a while yet. We'll waste an hour here, and let things quieten down. Well, it was a good sale. She must be congratulating herself.'

'No doubt she is,' agreed Vicente bitterly.

Marint gave him a shrewd glance. 'Don't look so glum, man. I suppose, knowing what you know, you wanted to stand up and forbid the sale. So did I, but there's not a thing we can do. If someone else won't take legal steps, that's all there is to it. Do you think that matters might be better for *La Hija* if they did?'

Vargas nodded. 'They certainly wouldn't be much worse.'

'You're exaggerating! What are a few horses, they're only animals! What's a house and land? Only stone and earth. What makes it any different from another house?'

'You don't feel like that, sir.'

'What I feel has no bearing on it. For all you know *La Hija* has decided to carry out her plans somewhere else. Perhaps she'll marry, and with a rich husband and her own money she can do as she pleases.'

'Why should she go? I've heard no talk of her marrying, and she doesn't want to leave Valdoro. She would hate it passing to anyone else. It's her mother who wants to be rid of it.'

'Are you sure of that?'

'Reasonably sure. But marriage –' he looked thoughtful. 'She wouldn't discuss that with me.'

Marint allowed himself to raise an eyebrow. Vargas's face flushed.

'It was her brother I knew well. That is why I think it's time something was done. After all, he was the Conde before he died.'

'But who's going to do it? It's out of your hands now.'

'It was never in them.'

'From what you've told me, it was once.'

'In a way – *Madre de Dios!* I still don't know if I did right.' Marint ground out his cigarette and stood up.

'*Hombre*, haven't you learned that one never knows? All a

137

man can do is what he thinks right at the time. There will be plenty of judgments. But if you listen to them, and query your actions afterwards, you're lost. Hindsight is the prerogative of theorists. For a man of deeds it's a luxury he can't afford, it saps his strength for every future decision. Sometimes the only thing to do is — forget. Now, let's justify our visit here and fill in a little time.'

At last everything was quiet. The buses had lumbered and rattled off, the cars had gone from the paddock.

In the patio Doña Luisa had graciously given a glass of wine to her agent and the auctioneers, and after a little conversation they, too, had left.

As the sound of car engines faded Doña Luisa, with a sigh of relief and satisfaction, walked through the long corridors into the main hall. She had been turning out a cabinet there; she might as well finish it before dinner.

For a moment she stood running her fingers lightly over the ormolu-encrusted fronts. This was one of the pieces of furniture she would keep. It was beautiful; quite valuable, too. And Fernando had been fond of it.

Fernando . . . her husband would never have sold Valdoro, but she must move with the times. The place was a white elephant to her. She opened the cabinet doors with a sharp movement. Fernando's memory was being irritatingly obtrusive today.

No doubt he would have handled Elena differently, but she had always been more amenable to him — and he was gone. And now, if Elena would not do as she was told, Valdoro must go.

With Fernando and Luis dead, Carlos had a right to his say as a relative besides being the prospective bridegroom. He thought it was necessary to be firm with Elena. She agreed with him, especially in view of what he had told her, that Elena had been meeting that jumped-up *vaquero*-turned-soldier behind her back — and going out with him in public! A stop would have to be put to that at once, or the girl would have no reputation left.

She felt hot with rage at the very thought of that visit to the Opera, and the way Carlos said it had been reported in the *Noticia.* Carlos had been very forbearing. As for Ana, she had long suspected her of having queer, unconventionally social-istic views, but for her to encourage Elena to meet that blackguard — it was outrageous! If she herself had known the facts when she had last met Ana, she would have had a great deal more to say.

And now the damage was done. One must hope to cover up as much as possible. Carlos seemed to be the only person willing to take definite steps to protect the family name.

She would most certainly do as he suggested. The engage-ment must be announced as soon as could be; Elena must be made to see it was the best — the only real — solution to their problems, and must be given no more opportunities to disgrace the family.

Now the horses were sold, perhaps Elena would realize that Valdoro would inevitably follow if the marriage did not go through. Carlos was convinced that would make Elena see reason, and that by this week-end they would be formally engaged.

Doña Luisa pulled the papers from the cabinet. They would all have to be sorted. But underneath them, at the back, was a large oblong box.

She drew it out and carried it to the table. It was made of polished mahogany with corners of brass, and on the lid an inset brass plate was engraved with a name.

Without stopping to read it, she knew it was the same name as that on the portrait over the mantelpiece, Miguel Moural, who had come to Riqueza from Spain, the first Moural de Valdoro. It was the case for his duelling pistols, which had hung on the chimney-breast flanking the portrait for longer than she had known Valdoro.

She might as well put the pistols away ready for packing for she wouldn't be parting with them. Standing in the broad hearth she lifted them down and laid them in the case, then with one last look she sat down, picked up some of the papers and began to examine them.

Surely that was a car? She paused, listening. It sounded as if someone was driving up to the main door. There was a knock on the outer door. If Carmela had not heard the car on its way round it would take minutes of thunderous knocking before she answered. Soon the knock was repeated. If Carmela did not come she would have to call her, she could not stand this steady banging.

Then to her surprise there were footsteps in the outer hall, and the inner door was pushed open. Doña Luisa looked up from her papers to see at the end of the room her uninvited visitor striding towards her. It was Gregor Marint.

'I see you have not yet learned to wait to be announced?'

Doña Luisa, irritated at the mere sight of the man she so hated, spoke as she would to an ill-trained domestic. Marint, quite unruffled, also dispensed with any formal greeting.

'I've learned not to waste time when the servant can't hear and the mistress won't heed. I came to see Señorita Moural.'

'Then you may leave as you came. She is not here.'

'You mean she is out riding? On what, might I ask?'

She ignored his sarcasm, and answered coldly, 'I mean she is not at Valdoro.'

'Not at Valdoro! When you've been selling her horses?'

'Not *her* horses, *my* horses.'

'I didn't mean the stud. I meant Estrella, and — '

She cut in on him contemptuously. 'I really do not know their names. But my agent tells me I have sold all my horses, as was my intention.'

Each gazed at the other, like two adversaries measuring the opposing strength.

At length Marint spoke. 'I can't believe Señorita Moural was in agreement with that.'

'What you believe is of no interest to me. Nor are my affairs any of your business, now that you have finished despoiling my estate.'

'Your affairs! I wouldn't waste a second's thought on them.

140

But I don't like seeing anyone treated the way you seem to be treating your daughter. Well, I shall find out the truth of the matter from Señorita Moural herself. I'll bid you good day.'

He was turning on his heel when her voice checked him.

'You can save yourself the trouble, General Marint. My daughter will not receive you.'

'Don't be too sure of that.'

'But I am sure.'

She looked at him levelly, with the faintest trace of a smile. She knew she must be utterly confident, she must convince him Elena had finished with him.

'You may not be aware of the fact, but this week-end my daughter will be formally engaged to her cousin, Don Carlos de Zurga. Any visit from you, even to extend your good wishes, would be more than unwelcome. In view of your reputation it would be scandalously inopportune.'

She saw his brows draw together in a sign of anger, but he answered her calmly enough.

'I prefer to let her and Señora Carvelo be the judges of that.'

'No doubt. But I am thinking of what will be reported, and conjectured, in the newspapers. My daughter now knows how unwise she was to be seen with you in public. I am sure she will be much more careful of her reputation now. If only for Don Carlos's sake she will not want to be known as one of the women you have chosen to amuse yourself with.'

He was holding his anger under control, but she saw his eyes narrow and his mouth tighten.

'Even a reporter with as dirty a mind as yours appears to be could hardly make anything out of my calling on her aunt. Once I am there I shall see her.'

How dare he insult her! He was staring at her, confronting her as if he were her equal. It was all the more infuriating since, as far as appearances went, he could well be so. He seemed to patronize the same tailor as her acquaintances — naturally he would want to — but he had no right to wear his clothes with comparable ease. He was a boor, a roughneck. He ought to look like one.

She jerked her mind back to the present problem. If he went back to Varena now, and called at the Avenida de Mayo tonight, there would be nothing to stop him seeing Elena. By Saturday or Sunday, with Elena at the de Zurga mansion, it would be easy to keep them apart, but now – she must delay him.

She gave him another scornful smile. 'You really think that after your recent behaviour my daughter will have anything to do with you? Your conceit must be unbounded!'

She was rewarded by a frown of annoyance. 'What are you talking about?'

She took a desperate gamble. 'We are not fools, General Marint. We know all about your visits to the Via Colón.'

She had struck in the dark, and the blow had gone home. He flashed her a look of incredulity which slowly turned to disgust. How amusing that he should be disgusted at being found out by her!

'You know about *that*?'

She nodded.

'Then what are you going to do about it?'

'Nothing. That is, nothing more. Elena's reaction will be enough. I simply wish to ensure that no other man distracts her from the marriage which has been arranged.'

For once it seemed that the situation was momentarily out of his grasp. He couldn't escape the fact that if Elena knew what he had been doing she would refuse to see him again. He must know her principles by now.

'*Dios*! I hand it to you. You find that out, and have the nerve to use it against me – when I meant no harm to her! And you'll do nothing more – you scheming bitch! You don't give a damn for anyone – not even your own daughter and her happiness. All you want is that she marries the fellow you pick. And I can imagine what governs your choice.'

His sudden vehemence, the brilliance of his eyes, the intensity of his expression were frightening. But after hearing him speak to her like that she felt she could do anything, no

142

matter how bold or desperate, to stop him. Yet in the face of insult she must keep her temper, or she might make a mistake.

'Señor de Zurga is entirely suitable. He will make her happy.'

'You mean he will make you rich, and her wretched. I can imagine what a nice fat marriage contract he must be proposing. You've missed your vocation, Señora Moural. You'd have made a fine madam. I'm surprised you didn't put another lot in the sale today, there were plenty of customers. If you'd auctioned off Elena at the same time as your bloodstock she might have made an even better price!'

Her heart thumped with fury until she felt sick and clutched the edge of the table, staring speechlessly at him. He went on looking at her with disgusted eyes, twisting his bitter-smiling mouth. She would make him pay for those words, that look!

Then he turned and walked away. She heard his feet fall crisply on the tiles as he made his way to the door. She must stop him.

'General Marint! Where are you going?'

She glanced around her as if the sight of something might give her an idea of what she could do. She was choking with rage and desperation. He did not even condescend to face her, but tossed his words over his shoulder.

'To see Elena. Where else?'

Then she saw what she must do. Yes, there would be justice in it, as well as revenge. She took one of the pistols out of the case. He was beginning to walk away again. She opened the box of percussion caps, removed one and held it in her hand.

'I advise you not to go.'

Something in her voice arrested him, and he turned round to see her with the pistol. He laughed. 'So you're threatening me! I suppose that's a compliment.'

'Unless you swear not to see my daughter I shall be obliged to shoot you.'

'What a melodrama! It won't wash, Señora. That pistol won't fire. And if it did, there's a penalty for murder.'

143

He was grinning. He seemed quite nonchalant. She would show him he had no reason to be.

'I shan't murder you. But I shall disable you, for this pistol will fire.'

'That would have unpleasant consequences – for you, if you hit me. *Can* you fire it? That's a flintlock – and you haven't even loaded it.'

He began to walk towards her. He was bluffing. He knew the pistols better than that, he wanted to get within distance so that he could rush her. But he was still a good fifteen paces away, with the end of the dining-table between them.

'Stand still. You know these pistols. They were flintlocks until they were converted. What you may not know is that for a long time they have been hanging up there, fully loaded with powder and ball, only needing the copper caps. You had better give me your word.'

He had halted, but now with a shrug he began to walk towards her again.

'My word? I'm surprised you could think of trusting it.'

She thumbed back the hammer and put the copper cap in place.

'Don't risk it. This is ready to fire.'

'Then fire away.'

'Don't think you can bluff me, General. I don't mind using these pistols. They are beautiful weapons – and incidentally my husband was very proud of their accuracy.'

'Did he give you target practice, Señora? I hope so. Women are such poor shots they're much more lethal when they're trying not to kill.'

His insolence was unbearable. He continued to stroll towards her. She raised the pistol. She must aim to disable, his death would be inconvenient; but with only one shot she must not miss.

'Don't see Elena!'

Still he came on. He must know she would shoot. He had no hope of disarming her before she could fire. A little nearer. She must be sure of hitting him.

144

'I shall see her.'

She lifted her hand.

He was smiling. His feet were moving evenly over the chequered tiles – if he reached that black one he would be near enough to jump and knock the gun aside. She straightened her arm. Still he came on. He was one step from the black tile. She fired.

CHAPTER TEN

Everything happened at once. There was the loud crack of the explosion, and the smell of gunpowder acrid in his nostrils as the ball caught him with a blow like a sledgehammer, knocking him off balance and sending him crashing to the floor. There was a rending, searing pain in his shoulder or chest or back or all three, and the heat and reek of his own blood on his clothes and body.

Looking up through the smoke which swirled in a blue haze over that end of the room he saw Señora Moural standing as if petrified, still holding the pistol.

He struggled to sit up, and pain rent at him increasingly. Finding his left arm useless he dragged it forward with his right hand under the elbow and managed to get into a sitting position.

'That was a damn fool thing to do,' he grunted.

Well, he wasn't dead, and his mind was still clear.

'Drop that pistol on the floor. When someone comes in, pick it up and put it on the table. Clean it as soon as you can. It was an accident. Remember that.'

She came to life and did as he said.

'Get some cloths, can't you? I'm bleeding like a stuck steer.'

She hurried to the door at the end of the hall, opened it and called, 'Carmela! Carmela!'

Then the door at the top by which he had entered was flung back and Vargas came in. His expression of horror was almost comic.

'It's all right. Help me to a chair. It was an accident.'

Señora Moural recognized her cue, picked up the pistol and placed it on the table. Vargas had got out a knife and was beginning to slit his coat sleeve.

'Here, Señora, do this while I get the First Aid kit from the jeep.'

He thrust the knife into her hand. Carmela appeared, took one look and began to scream.

'Stop squealing, woman! Get some sheets and clean towels. And hurry!'

Vargas ran out by one door as Carmela tottered through the other. It was like a French farce, except for the blood and broken bones, and they were real enough. The matriarch was making a poor job of cutting his coat away. She was a useless woman. And now, to add insult to injury, he would have to tidy up after her.

If she had thought what she was doing she wouldn't have been so quick on the trigger; in the few seconds before she fired he had visualized the possible consequences.

'Remember — it was an accident   I did it myself. We had better tell the same story.'

She bit her lip and said nothing. A glow of satisfaction spread in his mind. He had learned an all-important fact: that it was necessary to her to keep him from seeing Elena. So something was going on. It wasn't a simple sale of horses. It was to do with the marriage, he was sure of it. So that couldn't be entirely to Elena's liking. The matriarch thought that he, in some way or other, might prevent it. Then he'd make damn sure he did.

Vargas was coming in carrying the First Aid box. It was amusing to see how the emergency cancelled out his awe of Señora Moural. With an impatient sound he snatched the knife from her fingers and finished cutting away the coat and shirt from the left arm and chest.

'What's the damage, Vargas?'

'Your collar-bone's broken, sir.'

'I know that.'

'The ball went right through. It's made a mess of your back, but it's missed the artery. Still, there's quite a lot of bleeding.'

He knew that too. But he wasn't coughing blood, so his

147

lung must be all right. Oh, it wasn't bad at all. Now Carmela appeared, a pile of linen clutched to her billowing bosom, looking as if she would start screaming again as soon as she had enough wind.

Vargas turned to her. 'Give me that towel. Find a sheet. I want some long strips — roll them into bandages.'

The lad was doing quite well. He took a dressing from the kit and placed it on the entry wound below the shoulder.

'Hold this in place,' he ordered Señora Moural, and she did so. Then one on the back. 'And this.'

He rolled the towel into a pad and put it in Marint's armpit. raising the shoulder into place. Marint gritted his teeth. It wasn't pleasant. Then Vargas put the useless arm across his chest and proceeded to bandage everything in position with strips of sheet.

'That's the best I can do, sir. The sooner we can get you to a doctor the better.'

'Right. You can drive me back to Varena.'

'There is a doctor at Puenterojo,' suggested Señora Moural. It was the first intelligent remark she had made.

'He's the nearest and it's on the way,' Vargas added.

'You've done a good enough job. We'll get straight back.'

He could see Vargas bracing himself. 'Sir, I can't take that responsibility. You must see the doctor at Puenterojo.'

'There is no "must"!' he snapped.

Still, it wasn't fair to the lad. Nor was it sensible.

'Very well, if he's there I'll see him.'

He moved, then clenched his jaw, fighting a sudden increase of pain.

Vargas picked up the stained and tattered jacket and, draping it across Marint's shoulders, went to help him to his feet.

'Don't fuss, man! I can walk. I'm not shot in the leg. Oh, very well, give me an arm as far as the jeep.'

Vargas asked for rugs and Carmela was sent to get some.

He allowed himself to be settled with the rugs in the back of the jeep. There was just enough room to lie crosswise, it couldn't be called comfortable, but it would do. First thing in the morning he must see Elena.

The drive into Puenterojo demanded all Vicente's concentration, for the road was execrable. He dared not think of what he would do if the doctor was not at home. Marint should have immediate attention.

At last they were at the doctor's small whitewashed house. Vicente braked, switched off, jumped out and hammered on the door.

A little servant girl opened the door.

'The doctor, is he in? It's urgent.'

A woman's voice: 'What is it, María?'

The woman, presumably Señora Váldez, appeared.

'Señora, I have a wounded man — the doctor?'

'You're lucky. He got back five minutes ago.'

He helped Marint out of the back of the jeep and into the room Señora Váldez indicated.

'It's General Marint, surely?' Dr Váldez remarked calmly, as he pulled on a white jacket. 'What has happened?'

'I shot myself examining a pistol,' said Marint curtly.

Señora Váldez, now also white-coated, had water ready and the doctor washed his hands.

'Where? And at what time?'

'At Valdoro. An hour or more ago.'

Now they were removing the bandages, attending to the wounds.

The doctor spoke to Marint. 'What sort of shot was it?'

'A ball from an old duelling pistol.'

'I thought so. It's ploughed you up. A modern bullet would have drilled a much cleaner hole.'

'I'll remember that next time,' Marint responded drily.

'At least I am saved the trouble of removing it. It went in an upward path, ricocheted off the clavicle, breaking it. passing out through your back, fracturing the scapula. It is most fortunate the artery was not severed. This is merely immediate treatment. You will need more attention than I can

149

give you.'

'You'll be reporting this, I suppose?'

'It is a gunshot wound. By law the police must be informed.'

Vicente realized he had completely forgotten that aspect — the new law. Marint didn't miss a thing.

'When you've finished, would you give Señor Vargas a couple of sheets of paper? I want to dictate a statement.'

Without stopping his work the doctor indicated the desk to Vicente. 'Right hand top drawer.'

Vicente found paper and pen, sat down, and Marint began to dictate.

'I, Gregor Marint, wish to state that during a visit to Valdoro House I accidentally shot myself when examining an antique pistol. No blame attaches to anyone else. Have you got that, Vargas? Right. Make another copy. When I'm strapped up I'll sign them, and you and the doctor can witness my signature.'

'I will witness the signature,' remarked Dr Váldez. 'I cannot attest the facts as I was not present.'

Marint glanced up at him, but said nothing. Dr. Váldez straightened up. 'That is all I can do with my limited facilities.'

He turned to his wife. '*Querida*, will you see if María has coffee ready? We shall need plenty of it.'

She nodded, took off her coat and left the room.

'You have lost some blood, General, so you must replace that fluid. I shall give you weak coffee, you must not have anything too stimulating.'

'Thank you, Doctor. You've been very good. I'll be glad of the coffee. Then we'll be on our way.'

'Where do you propose to go, General?'

'Back to Varena.'

'That distance — in a jeep — in your condition? That would be unwise.'

'Don't make me sound like a pregnant woman! You know there's no train until tomorrow.'

'I'm not suggesting the train. An ambulance can come out

150

for you.'

Marint's eyebrows shot up. 'Would an ambulance come out for a *peón* who was in my state?'

'You are not a *peón,* General Marint. You are public property, and it's my duty to safeguard you. And I would not enjoy putting a *peón* on the train as you are, even if it were necessary.'

'Public property, am I? That's a new one. Well, Vargas is a good watchdog, and a good driver.'

At this point Vicente felt entitled to intervene.

'Dr Váldez, could the General stay here tonight? Couldn't you make arrangements for an ambulance to come out early tomorrow?'

'That's what I had in mind. Then he must go directly to hospital, he will need further attention.'

Marint's voice took on a sergeant-major rasp. 'I am going back to Varena tonight.'

'In that case, Señor Vargas, you must deliver him to the hospital without delay.'

'Stop talking about me as if I were a parcel! I can see a doctor in the morning.'

'General Marint, you are my patient. I shall dictate your treatment until you are in other hands. Unless, of course, you are prepared to risk being left with a partial disability in your shoulder and arm?'

Marint gave a wry grin. 'You're right, so I'll meet you halfway. But I have reasons for wanting to get back at once. I must go.'

'Very well. I will let Señor Vargas drive you, provided you go straight to hospital. I will get in touch and warn them to expect you.'

He lifted the identity disc which hung on a silver chain round Marint's neck.

'Your blood group? Ah, yes. Not a particularly rare one, that is good; they may want to have a transfusion ready.' He moved to the door. 'I will telephone now, it may take a little while to get through.'

151

As he closed the door Marint's glance fell on the statements. 'I'll sign those now,' he said.

Vicente handed them to him. What had the doctor said? 'I'll witness the signature, but I cannot attest the facts —'

He turned and picked up the remains of Marint's jacket. There was not so much blood on the front — there was the bullet-hole, the pale fawn material stained brownish-red — he looked from it to Marint, who was regarding him steadily, his expression calm, non-committal. How slow he had been. The doctor had guessed.

'Sir, that statement — I can't sign it,' he said quietly.

'Why not?'

'Because it's not true, sir.'

Suddenly words rushed from him. 'It wasn't an accident. Señora Moural shot you. I was a fool not to see it at once. *Why protect her*? She isn't worth it!'

Marint's eyes held him, they were hard and bright.

'Protect *her*? No! Think, boy! If I'm wounded by anyone else, even accidentally, there must be a police enquiry. And the papers will report it. Now there was no one else about but you. It's got to be Señora Moural, even the servant will have to admit it. But the Señora has a daughter, and I have been seen with that daughter. If Señora Moural shoots me, what will the papers think? They are always ready for a scandal. *Do you want it suggested that I've seduced La Hija*?'

'*Madre de Dios!*'

Vargas felt the blood leaving his face, felt himself going cold. Marint was right. In its present mood, the anti-Government press, which was muck-raking for all it was worth, would find such a conclusion delightfully inevitable. Once again any stick would do to beat Marint with. Why should the newspapers care if an innocent girl caught half the blows?

And Elena — he could imagine the disgusting conjecture. She would be at the mercy of all the salacious gossip and dirty innuendo. What was more, she would be despised and cold-shouldered by the bulk of her acquaintances, for Marint was a man of such personality, how many people would believe her innocent? She would never shake off the stigma, it would be social murder for her.

It was several seconds before he could find words.

'My apologies, General. Your statement must be correct.'

Vicente stared through the windscreen at the band of light cut by the headlamps in the surrounding dark. On one hand, he knew, was uneven rolling countryside, on the other, vast plantations; somewhere down on his left the river ran, but there was not enough moon yet for it to be visible. The land was levelling out, and they would be losing height steadily all the way to the capital. But the road surface was little better as yet, and the road was all that concerned him.

He couldn't think why the General had insisted on getting back to Varena that night. If the President had asked for him he would have said so, and there was nothing at the Ministry which could not wait until the afternoon, so what was the hurry? It seemed sheer folly to chance the journey at night in the jeep.

The road was deserted; they might travel mile after mile without seeing so much as a cabin – which would be empty until harvest – and if they had a blow-out or ran off the road they would get no help until the first passer-by found them in the morning. And the General was hardly in a fit state for this sort of travelling. Vicente was praying again, 'Mother of God, give us a safe journey'.

He wasn't sleepy, he was too strung up for that. Normally the drive would not have bothered him, tiring though it was. But night-time which made it so much more difficult also immeasurably increased its hazards, and the discomfort of a rough ride was now magnified into acute pain and possible danger for the General.

Every half-hour, as Dr Váldez had instructed, he stopped, went to the rear, helped Marint to sit up, gave him a drink from the bottle of lukewarm coffee and checked the bandages for signs of any sudden flow of blood. Settling Marint back again he told him the mileage, then the journey continued. On they went, on and on, and his whole life seemed to be narrowed down to a track spinning and lurching towards him through the headlights' beams.

Vicente felt as if the devil were sitting beside him in the cab. If Marint died, how varied and appalling the consequences would be. A murder charge for the Señora. Scandal and disgrace for Elena. Censure for himself. But death for the General. No, not this way, not such a death for such a man . . .

He drove with the cold hand of fear gripping his heart.

CHAPTER ELEVEN

Don Pablo had in fact taken some notice of Doña Ana since he had sent an invitation to Elena to spend the week-end with them. Elena had accepted, knowing that it had been extended so that she could meet and make up with her mother, which she wanted to do, although she was still very angry over the sale of the horses, but she had been by no means overjoyed at his suggestion that Carlos should call for her at the office and drive her back to lunch with them.

Knowing how conventional Don Pablo was, she could only interpret this as a contrived *tête-à-tête* — an unpleasant omen as it showed he had not quite given up his marriage schemes for them both. In addition, she would not have the pleasure and support of Doña Ana's presence; although invited, she had considered it politic to keep out of her sister-in-law's way for a little longer in order not to jeopardize Elena's chances of reconciliation.

Apart from the possible peacemaking, the week-end which promised to be boring if not actually distasteful would be a waste of time. So Elena left the Avenida de Mayo carrying her week-end case and finding the prospect of the next two days very little to her taste.

On the bus she found her feelings changing, becoming tinged with a faint sense of impending disaster. There were never many passengers at this stage; the few that were on board usually sat together in the front and carried on animated discussions between themselves and the driver.

But this morning everybody was subdued, they all talked in low voices as if concerned over something. She thought she heard the words 'the General'; a few moments later, quite clearly, she heard Marint's name.

155

So there *was* something wrong, and what was more, it had already become public knowledge and common gossip. It must be serious; from their manner. But she had heard nothing the previous evening, whatever it was must have been on the radio that morning for it to be general talk, the papers did not come out in the suburbs so early.

They were running into the city now, and there, outside a shop, was a placard: GENERAL MARINT — CRITICAL. But *what* was critical? Was he critical of something, or was it his own position which was in danger? There had been no warning of any political rift

It was mysterious, and she found it disconcerting to be so completely in the dark. There was a news-stand by her alighting point, and she felt a gnawing impatience to reach the end of her journey.

She got off the bus and pushed her way into the knot of people buying papers A man's voice said close to her: 'They say he was shot —'

And another: 'That's what I heard.'

Her stomach lurched with fear. She thrust her coins at the paper boy.

'*Noticia* — anything — ' and took what he gave her.

She did not need to search, the thick headlines leaped out at her: GENERAL IN SHOOTING ACCIDENT.

She was being jostled by other people coming for papers, her hand was shaking, she could not read the smaller print. She hurried along a few paces, and putting her case down by a shop window she stood there, her paper clenched in both hands, trying to take in what was underneath the headlines.

Frantically she turned to the Stop Press. *General Marint — condition still critical.*

Madre de Dios, what was it all about?

At the time of going to press no official statement has been received, but it is understood that General Gregor Marint was admitted to the Hospital de Nuestra Señora de Merced in the early hours of the morning, unconscious and in a critical condition.

156

From our reporter on the spot.

General Marint, who was carried from a jeep into the hospital on a stretcher at 1.30 this morning, was unconscious and appeared to have been wounded in the shoulder or chest, suffering severe loss of blood. No details were given in answer to my enquiries, but I was told that the General sustained a gunshot injury during a visit to Valdoro State Farm. I was assured that this was accidental.

He received medical attention and was considered fit to travel, but during the journey his condition suddenly deteriorated. Doctors who had been previously alerted began their fight for his life immediately he reached Nuestra Señora de Merced.

The Editor has been requested to stress that the hospital should not be telephoned for news of the General's condition. Frequent bulletins will be issued.

Elena leaned against the shop wall, her knee joints felt as if they had turned to jelly, her heart was pounding, her throat swelling and tightening.

'Isn't it dreadful?'

The voice was vaguely familiar. She lifted her head from the paper, and saw Rosa Santos beside her. Rosa worked at the office with Elena.

'I heard it on the radio at breakfast time. They're giving bulletins every hour.'

'What do they say? How is he now?'

The newspaper went to press hours ago, she felt desperate for more recent news.

'Much the same. Still grave, they say. I wonder what happened?'

Rosa's face was serious, her eyes, moist and sad, gazed into Elena's. It doesn't matter what happened, she thought frantically, all that counts is, will he live? She shook her head. Somehow it didn't seem real — and yet it was.

Rosa was looking at her curiously. 'You know him, don't you?'

'Yes.'

'He's such a wonderful man. It's awful.'

Elena felt Rosa's hand on her arm. 'Look at the time. We must be going to the office — and you could do with a sit down and a cup of coffee.'

Like a stopped clock that starts ticking again when given a shake, her brain seemed to work once more at Rosa's touch.

'You go. I shall be late.'

Rosa's eyes widened.

'Please — will you take my case, Rosa? I must go to the hospital. Tell Señor Kelly I'll come back when I can.'

Rosa's eyes lit up.

'Of course! Of course you must go! I do hope you'll find him better. Look, there's a taxi.'

But Elena was already waving at the driver. 'Thank you, Rosa. The hospital. Nuestra Señora.'

She bluffed her way past the hospital reception desk by giving her full name. The word 'Valdoro' acted like a pass key, and she was allowed to see the Sister in whose care Marint had been placed.

Two men in white coats were standing in front of an observation window; the Sister, sitting behind her desk, looked up, a little surprised. She was middle-aged, with a very efficient air. Mother of God, give her a kind heart. Elena prayed.

'I am Elena Moural de Valdoro. Would you please let me see General Marint?'

The Sister looked more surprised. 'I'm afraid that's quite impossible, Señorita Moural. He is barely conscious. Of Valdoro, you said? Were you there when it happened? Can you tell us — ?'

The two men turned to look at her.

'No, I wasn't there. Oh, please, let me see him.'

One of the men came forward. He was thin, with a high forehead and tired, kind eyes.

'Señorita Moural, I am Dr Lobos. You did say Señorita *Elena* Moural?'

'Yes.'

He glanced at the other doctor. 'It's the same name. it's worth a chance,' he said cryptically, and then gave her a smile.

'Don't worry, Señorita, We are doing all we can, and he is holding his own.'

She felt grateful for his humanity.

'You may see him for a moment, but please do not excite him. I think he has been asking for you.'

The ward was overlooked by the observation window, a private ward with only one bed in it. Marint was not in the bed but on a stretcher trolley, with a nurse standing beside him. He was covered to the chin with a grey blanket, but white bandages were visible over the left shoulder, for the left arm was held out from the body on a metal brace. Next to the trolley transfusion apparatus was dripping blood into his right arm.

All this Elena registered vaguely, while her gaze and all her conscious attention was focused on Marint's face.

He was dreadfully pale, his tanned skin looked yellowish, his mouth was drained of colour and he was breathing in short gasps through his parted lips. His chin was dark with stubble, and oddly enough this wrung Elena's heart as much as his obvious bodily distress, for it seemed to underline his helplessness. His eyes were closed. She did not know whether he was conscious; she thought not.

The nurse moved aside, and she approached the trolley to stand looking down at him.

'Gregor,' she said quietly, and then again: 'Gregor.'

His eyelids flickered and lifted. He looked up blankly, then slowly his eyes focused on her. The fingers of his right hand twitched slightly on the grey blanket, and instinctively she clasped them gently in her own. They answered her with momentary pressure.

He smiled. 'Hoped — you'd — come — '

His voice jerked out, low and rasping, on the outflow of his gasping breaths.

'Don't talk, Gregor. Just rest,' she answered softly.

'Must -- talk. Doña Raquel I went — but — not — to

159

hurt — you.'

Was he wandering? Had he been operated on, and were the drugs still confusing him? His eyes were staring at her as if imploring her to understand him. Every word was an effort, it must be important to him. She must pretend to know what he meant, or he would get excited, exert himself too much.

'Yes, Gregor, it's all right.' *But who was Doña Raquel?*

'Forgive — all — I've said — and done?'

'Gregor, it was nothing, nothing to make a fuss about.'

He smiled again, and looked more contented. 'All I've said' must refer to their quarrel — but what had he done? She could not make head or tail of it. But he hadn't finished. His fingers moved within her hand, his eyes were questioning her.

'You — love — de Zurga?'

So that mattered to him.

'No. I never have. I never could.'

The eyelids drooped in satisfied acceptance, then lifted again and his eyes gazed at her intently.

'Don't — marry — him.' His voice was thick, the gasping breaths came quicker.

'I won't.'

He forced out one more word. 'Promise?'

'I promise, Gregor.'

His eyes closed, his fingers relaxed. She thought he had lapsed into unconsciousness. Dr Lobos came forward. 'That is long enough, Señorita. We have to take the General for further treatment.'

'Thank you very much for letting me see him.' She paused. 'What are his chances, Doctor?'

He looked at her thoughtfully.

'The fact that he is still alive shows he has a good chance. Another X-ray may tell us something more. We shall do everything possible, you can be sure of that, Señorita Moural, and he is a fighter, that is a great thing.'

She thanked him and went blindly out of the hospital. To tell her that they would do everything possible sounded like a death-knell to her. 'A good chance' — that was all the doctor could give Gregor. He was a fighter, yes, but in his state would that be enough?

She was shattered by the experience of seeing him in that condition. He was so vigorous, so strong, it was an offence against nature that an accident could have reduced him to this.

She began to realize how devastating and complete her loss would be if he died. She had tried to accept the fact that it was unlikely they would even remain close friends, but at least, he would be there. She would follow his career, take pleasure in his success, be proud of all he did for the country. It would be some compensation. But if he were to die, she would have nothing.

She had been walking without knowing where she was going; she found herself outside a church.

She went in; the candle-lit gloom closed about her. She crossed herself, lit a candle, knelt down and prayed. After a few minutes she could think of no more prayers, she could no longer blot out the memory of Gregor's stricken face. She was racked by the thought that it might be the last time she would see him alive; she found that she was weeping violently. It was more than a minute before she could control herself; then she tried to pray once again for his safety.

She stood up. There were other people in the church, women of all ages, and a few men, all she felt sure praying for Gregor. All over the country it must be the same, for many more people loved him than hated him. She believed in the power of prayer, she must believe that he would live. She would go back to the office and try to be confident. He would expect it of her.

'Well, Elena, so this is where you work!'

Carlos de Zurga took in the office with a glance in which condescension was nicely mixed with a strained tolerance.

'It's even smaller than I expected.'

'We don't need much space,' Elena answered, covering her typewriter. 'We only do the paperwork here.'

'There's not much of that, surely?' he retorted blandly.

161

'We keep busy. Excuse me.

She picked up her folder and went to the inner office, leaving him lounging against her desk, being covertly quizzed by Rosa and Señor Gomez.

'The last letters, Señor Kelly.' She placed them for him to sign. 'May I leave now? Everything is finished.'

'Certainly, Señorita Moural. And there is no need to come in on Monday, if you don't feel up to it.'

'Thank you very much. But I expect to be here.'

Carlos took her case. He had parked his car outside, not too conveniently for the traffic. A nearby policeman took a long look at him but did nothing. They swung out into the moving stream, and Carlos switched on the radio. The station was broadcasting serious music. He gave a mock groan.

'I suppose, while the hero of the people is laid low, we shall be fed on a diet of this stuff. What a prospect!' His hand was on the switch. 'Oh well, I dare say it's better than nothing.'

He left it on. How like him, thought Elena. Only Carlos would expect the station to broadcast gay and trivial music when the country's first soldier was fighting for his life. Carlos became more objectionable each time they met.

She sat well apart from him on the bench seat, avoiding the slightest contact. While Carlos progressed with the customary lack of courtesy which he considered dashing driving, Elena felt her spine stiffening with resentment. She stole a glance at her watch. In a few minutes there would be a bulletin.

'We expect Aunt Luisa this afternoon. You'll be anxious to hear how the bloodstock sale went.'

'Not at all. The horses are sold. I have no more interest in the matter.'

The music stopped.

"*Here are the news flashes*,' the announcer's voice began. '*The condition of Gen –* '

Carlos's finger had flipped off the switch.

She clenched her hands in her lap, gritted her teeth, and said nothing. They drove on in silence. Then: 'Oh, I'm sorry, Elena.' He made a smooth pretence at an apology. 'Did you

162

want the news?'

'It doesn't matter.' It was probably too late now
I should have asked you. How foolish of me.'

He switched it on again.

' – *further bulletin in an hour's time.*'

She saw him smooth out the suspicion of a smile from the corners of his mouth.

The *gran sala* in the de Zurga mansion was rarely used. and looking around her Elena did not find that surprising. The whole house was gloomy and oppressive. but this large room on the first floor was the stiffest, most unwelcoming apartment she could ever remember seeing.

It looked as if it had remained unaltered since Don Pablo's father's day. After the white and panelled walls of Valdoro the effect of papering, which far too many years ago had smothered the surfaces with ornate leaves and flowers and scrolls in shades of ochre and sepia on a background reduced by time to an indeterminate pale mud colour, was both fussy and depressing, and made the large ornate pieces of mahogany furniture look unnecessarily cumbersome.

The overstuffed couches and chairs were covered in a heavy dark green brocade, much faded where it had caught the light. The unfortunate wallpaper was overpoweringly hung with pictures. There were oil-paintings of religious subjects, family portraits of an amazing woodenness, and examples of still life. There were ornaments too, far too many, ranging from a glass case of wax fruit to a china shepherdess with a ferocious simper and a very fancy crook.

If I lived here I'd smash that for a start, Elena thought, and then returned to wondering why Carlos had asked for a private interview with her.

Remembering the last time they had been alone she had practically refused point-blank, but she had thought better of it. She must try to see the week-end through without antagonizing anyone, though after a bare three hours she was already finding it difficult.

In another hour or so her mother would be arriving — what sort of a meeting would that be? What could she say to her? She tried to concentrate on that. She must keep her mind occupied, for as soon as her thoughts wandered she saw Gregor Marint gasping for breath, his body racked, his face with that deathly pallor. And she could do nothing but wait for the next bulletin and pray for an improvement.

She must stop thinking about Gregor.

What did Carlos want? She had been waiting nearly five minutes. What did he think he was doing?

Then she heard footsteps, and turned away from the window with its view of flagged paths and dark shrubs as the door latch clicked and Carlos entered the room.

He shut the door carefully behind him and came towards her. She waited for him to speak. He indicated the couch. She chose a straight-backed chair and sat down. He stood in front of her, his black eyes gazing at her challengingly. He said nothing. She began to feel impatient.

'Well, Carlos, what did you want to see me about?'

He took out his gold cigarette case, picked out a cigarette, returned the case, brought out a lighter and, without asking her permission, she noticed, lit the cigarette. She determined not to speak again until he did, and if he kept her waiting much longer she would leave the room.

He enjoyed a couple of puffs, inhaling deeply. Then he smiled. 'I trust, Elena, you will have no objection if I announce our engagement this evening at dinner?'

She was completely taken aback, then surprise gave way to indignation. She stood up. 'You must realize that you are wasting your time. And mine.'

He grasped her shoulder. His suavity had left him.

'Don't be in such a hurry. You don't deny that you are infatuated with Gregor Marint?'

She faced up to him, determined to admit nothing.

'If I were infatuated with half-a-dozen men, or with none at all, it would make no difference to my feelings for you. I dislike you, Carlos, and I am beginning to despise you. Since

164

you don't love me, why not stop this nonsense?'

He paled as he stared down at her.

'You love Gregor Marint,' he said slowly. 'Very well. I'll show you what sort of a man he is. Can you love a lecher?'

'Get out of my way!'

'You are going to listen to me. I am going to cure you of this obsession. I am not asking you to take my word alone. I am going to give you proof -- and from someone who has no interest in the matter — that he is not fit for decent society.'

'You can keep your proofs. And your marriage contract. I am not interested in either.

He caught her by both shoulders and stood over her. For a sickening moment she thought he was going to put his arms round her, but instead he forced her down into a chair. His eyes were shining, his face unnaturally pale.

'You are going to listen.'

He went to the door, opened it and called out an instruction to someone in the hall below. When he turned she had risen and was standing nearby ready to walk out of the room. He caught her by the wrist.

'Do you want me to hold you while you listen? I am quite prepared to do so.'

'I'm sure you are. No doubt you enjoy using force on a woman.'

She looked up at him contemptuously. The sallow face, set in an expression of anger, changed to a smile.

'When it is necessary,' he agreed. 'So you are afraid to face the truth?' He urged her back into the chair, she would not condescend to struggle with him. 'You know what he is like, but you don't relish hearing chapter and verse? Is that it?'

There was a tap on the door.

A young man entered, small and slim. He was not well-dressed enough to be a friend of Carlos; in fact there was a general air of seediness about him. Was the strain telling on her? Elena wondered. The sight of this stranger seem to add to her confusion.

'This is Señor López, a private enquiry agent.'

The young man made a small bow to Elena, she looked from Carlos to him and back again in mystification.

'For the last two weeks, on my instructions, Señor López has been keeping track of the movements of General Marint.'

She gazed at Carlos incredulously. 'You mean you had him watched, *spied on*?'

'I had him watched.'

'It's infamous!'

'It was necessary. Señor López, your records.'

From his pocket the silent young man pulled out a small notebook.

'This is a true statement of what you yourself observed, or discovered?'

'It is.'

At last, reluctantly it seemed, he had spoken.

'Kindly hand it to Señorita Moural.'

As López did so, Carlos spoke to her in a silky voice. 'Now, will you please read the entries marked in red?'

I love him, I believe in him, she thought wildly. To read this is a betrayal, it is as if I doubted him. But if I don't –

The book was opened for her, Carlos's long finger with the smooth, well-manicured nail pointed out the first entry. Several lines under the same date were unmarked; a large red cross was placed against the time 19.30, and the words: *G.M. left his apartment, took a taxi to the Plaza Colón. Walked down the Via Colón to the new apartment building. Went to Apartment 3 on the first floor. Was admitted by a young woman. Stayed about one hour.*

Steel herself as she might, she felt something approaching panic surge over her. Gregor's private life was none of their business, what did Carlos think he could prove?

'Read on.'

Her eyes were dragged down to the page again where López had added his comments:

Made enquiries re identity of occupant of Apartment 3. Apartment held in the name of Señor Santilla, but occupied by Doña Raquel Mendoza, a good-looking woman in her late

166

twenties, said to be a widow. She lives there alone, with a daily maid. Is sometimes visited by Señor Santilla, a middle-aged man, reputed to be a relative. He stays overnight.

Doña Raquel — and Gregor — what is the sense of it? she was thinking, when Carlos's voice was in her ear again as his hand turned the page.

'Now the other marked entries.'

There were three more, each one recording an evening visit to Señora Mendoza in the Via Colón.

'Notice the dates.'

With a shock she realized the first was that of the Monday two days after Gregor had left Valdoro in a rage at their quarrel.

'Four meetings in a fortnight, you see.'

He took the notebook from her and spoke to López.

'You swear this is a true record?'

'Yes.'

'You have a copy of it in a safe place?'

'Yes.'

'That is all I shall require of you at present.'

López shot her a look, deprecating and apologetic. and left them.

Carlos stood there, smiling slightly, holding the book in his right hand and tapping it on the palm of his left. He was feeling confident. Elena was plainly shaken by what he had shown her, but she looked at him steadily, trying to put a bold face on it, he guessed.

'It means nothing to me. except that you have overstepped all the bounds of decent behaviour by having someone spied on!'

All right, he would teach her to be defiant.

'It is not *my* behaviour which is in question. but Marint's! He appears to like variety in his women. Not so long ago he was meeting you, taking you out to luncheon. And now here he is. visiting a high-class prostitute.'

'That's a filthy thing to say!' She looked sick with shock. 'And you have no grounds.'

167

The blood had rushed to her cheeks. He watched her with satisfaction.

'No grounds! I could hardly be plainer! This woman is young and good-looking, living in an apartment provided by a middle-aged protector. But the protector is often away. Being what she is, she feels free to sell her favours elsewhere. And Marint takes advantage of it. Are you really surprised he goes to such a woman? We've all heard of his amorous propensities — I quite expected him to visit a brothel.'

He dropped all polite pretences, the manners of their conventional society going by the board; he was using any weapon and wounding her as deeply as he could. And he was enjoying it.

'It's all lies. It can't be true. There are a dozen possible explanations.'

'Give me one.'

'Why should I? I don't need to make excuses for him.'

'But you do — if there are any.'

He stubbed out his cigarette and spoke with studied casualness. 'López tells me they were strangers at their first meeting. She opened the door herself, and he asked for her by name. She invited him in at once.'

'All right. They were strangers. That doesn't make either of them immoral.'

'It is touching to find you standing up for him, but you must see that your loyalty is misplaced. You had far better face the facts.'

She would not give ground. 'The only facts are that he has made a few innocent evening visits.'

'*Innocent*! You'll go a long way before you find anyone to agree with that. Just think about it for a moment — and remember that he always goes in the evenings when the servant has left and she is alone.'

He lit another cigarette. She sat proudly, not answering.

'One of these days you will thank me for destroying your little illusions. Now you know the truth you can soon be rid of the infatuation.'

168

She stood up. The flush had left her face, she was now very pale. Surely that must be the end of it. She wouldn't take any more from Marint now it was plain that the fellow was visiting a hired woman, and someone else's mistress into the bargain. He, Carlos, was a man of the world, but he found the situation contemptible So what would she, a sheltered high-class girl, think of it?

She looked sick. She was shocked, no doubt of it. Now he could afford to be conciliatory.

'Forget about him, Elena. Marry me, and take what I can give you. Keep Valdoro, we can have it between us — '

He put his arm around her, his other hand began to caress her shoulder. She threw her head back and looked at him, bewildered. Then she gathered herself together and tried to push him away.

'No, I don't believe it. And you shan't have Valdoro — or me!'

So, she was still resisting him! He caught her wrists and drew her hands down, holding her struggling body against him.

'For Marint's sake, keep quiet and listen.'

It worked. She took a gasping breath, but made no other sound.

'Don't you agree with me, that the newspapers — and their readers — will be most interested to know where Marint has been spending some of his spare time?'

Now she looked more startled than angry. 'I don't understand you.'

'I know more than one editor who would pay a lot to publish López's notebook. It would make good reading. Quite an exposé — the people's idol showing his feet of clay! The irresistible Marint going to a prostitute — from choice or necessity! Even an *expensive* harlot tarnishes the image, don't you think? Much better if he'd simply kept a mistress.'

She had gone quite white. 'You mean you'd give that notebook to a newspaper? They would never publish it — particularly now.

Such a poor bluff, he was almost sorry for her.

'Wouldn't they? They'd jump at it! Apart from the public reaction, consider the political side of it. The President expects the members of his government, particularly his Ministers to be above suspicion or reproach. A juicy little scandal in Marint's private life would cost him the Ministry, I should think. A man can get away with a lot provided he's discreet, but a known disgrace like that and his public life is over. I suppose he *might* be allowed to retain his Army rank ... Oh, it's a valuable document, not only to an editor, but to some politicians.'

She gasped. 'Are you suggesting that you'd sell it to his political oponents?'

He shook his head, waiting while she registered relief. 'I have no need to be mercenary. I'd give it.'

Her voice was sinking to a whisper. 'But he is so ill — no one would publish that at such a time — when he can't defend himself — '

He allowed himself a smile. 'My dear Elena, newspaper men and politicians are not famed for their nobility. They are interested in circulation, in sensation, and in power, and they would love the impact of that story. Believe me, they would read into it everything I have, and a great deal more. They might well link it with his injury. Sooner or later someone is bound to say that, in view of this scandal, the shooting was no accident. That he knew he was going to be exposed, so he shot himself deliberately because he couldn't face the consequences — or to get some public sympathy.'

Now she was wide-eyed with horror.

'No! No one could believe he would do that!'

'How naïve you are! But don't look so worried. There is no need for such an occasion to arise.'

'No — no, you couldn't be so cruel.'

'Of course not. I will give you the notebook to destroy.'

He smiled again. 'As soon as we are married.'

She had agreed. There was nothing else she could do. If she had not done so, Carlos would have sent his story where it would do the most damage, and long before Gregor was well enough to disprove it the filthy rumour would have taken hold. If he died, there would be one more smear on his name which might never be wiped away.

Carlos's attack on Gregor, and his method of carrying it out, had been so unexpected that at first she had been confused, almost numbed. For a few seconds she had, in her surprise, nearly believed him. It had been so circumstantial.

The meetings had started just after the quarrel at Valdoro. And Gregor had tried to tell her. As she struggled to collect her thoughts she kept seeing his face, yellowed, drawn, bearded, with staring eyes and parted lips, kept hearing his gasping words,

'Doña Raquel – I went – but not to hurt you – .'

Why should he try to tell her? Wasn't it an apology? An apology for what? Could Carlos conceivably be right? Could Gregor have left her in a state of frustrated physical desire and gone to some woman he had never met, but who was willing to satisfy him as she had not?

The idea was revolting, but she knew enough about men to realize it was a possibility. No, not Gregor! Something in her cried out. He wouldn't do that. He is passionate, but not like that. He wanted me, because of what I am, not because he is an animal. *Dios*, don't let me think of it – but why, why did he mention Doña Raquel? Why tell me of his visits to the Via Colón?

'Forgive – all I've said – and done – .'

It all seemed so damning.

She could not hide her shock and disgust from Carlos, but she had, she hoped, concealed her rage. Slowly it had welled up within her, swamping all other emotions, a hot fury, a burning resentment at such treatment both of herself and Gregor.

Somehow she hid her anger, and agreed to the bargain without the slightest intention of keeping her word. If he could play a dirty game, then so could she. Let him think he had won; be submissive, a little afraid, and all the while gain time, time for Gregor to recover, if necessary time for her to set about finding the truth of the story – though how she might do that she had not the faintest idea.

She could only think of one person who might be able to help her. Vicente. And that was a long shot. He was Marint's subordinate, not his intimate. But if she could only see him he might help.

Then she found that Carlos had given some thought to the situation. He made it plain that, if Elena mentioned the true facts of their engagement to anyone else, the story would be released. He wished his father and her mother to think he had won her over. She was considerably shaken when he produced a Bible and instructed her to swear on it that she would not communicate anything in any way to Marint.

'I've no doubt he mustn't be excited at present, and won't be allowed to open his own letters for some little while; nevertheless, one can't be too careful. So put your hand on the Book and swear to it.'

She could have struck him. He knew what a Bible oath meant to her. Having no scruples himself he could exploit those of other people to the full.

'Come along. Swear.'

She took the Bible and swore the oath.

'Good. Now I can announce our engagement at dinner.'

Her mother arrived. Their meeting was cool, but no worse. The rest of the day dragged on until dinner time.

Sitting at table Elena had no appetite; she had to force the food down, her mouth was dry, every morsel was as unmanageable as it was unpalatable to her.

Carlos said nothing about the engagement, keeping her on tenterhooks, eyeing her with covert speculation as the small talk in which no one was really interested was passed languidly to and fro. At last, when they were finishing dessert, he seemed to decide the time had come. He raised his voice so that everyone round the table should listen.

'I have some news for you all, and especially for Father and

172

Aunt Luisa. I am very happy to tell you that this afternoon Elena accepted my proposal of marriage.'

Don Pablo leaned forward, the heavy eyelids lifted, the sombre features lit up.

'So . . . ! You have persuaded her at last. Good boy!' Then to Elena: 'You make me very happy, my dear. This is what I have wanted for a long time.'

He looked round the table. 'Well, everybody, isn't it grand news?' He heaved himself to his feet. 'Let's drink to their health. Carlos and Elena!'

When everyone had drunk, Doña Luisa remarked, 'I am glad you have made up your mind at last, Elena. It's a pity you didn't decide a little earlier. If I had known I would have given you the pick of half a dozen horses from the sale as a wedding present. Now they have all gone.'

'Never mind, Luisa,' Don Pablo cut in, his manner positively jovial. 'Elena shall have all the horses she wants. There's plenty of stable room here, and she can take her choice from those on the *estancia*. Manuel has some good horseflesh there. You're looking quite pale, my dear! Don't tell me you're nervous, because I'm sure Carlos wants to marry you as soon as possible! Then he'll cure your nerves in a good old-fashioned way, won't you, my boy?'

Doña Luisa looked shocked, and Enrique, embarrassed; Maddalena laughed, Carlos smiled darkly. Elena sat, gripping her hands under the table, trying not to register anything. Not to think, not to feel.

'Of course there is no point in delaying the marriage,' her mother was saying. 'It must be in the Cathedral, naturally; all the de Zurgas and Mourales marry there – so it will take a few weeks to arrange. Usually six, I think. But we can use the time. After all, we have a complete trousseau to get.'

Don Pablo was nodding agreement. 'The legal side can be settled in an afternoon. We have discussed all the important points and made most of the decisions.'

In other words, thought Elena, all the preliminary haggling is over, my price is already settled.

'Quite so,' her mother concurred. 'Well, Elena, at least you are in time to save Valdoro. I don't mind admitting I had decided it was too much of a tie and responsibility for me. I was intending to put it up for sale on the open market this week. But now I shall come to some arrangement with your uncle, so that you and Carlos can have the use of it, and it will eventually come to the two of you.'

Am I supposed to say thank you? Elena thought, anger boiling up within her again. Valdoro is more mine than yours, and however you put it you're selling me and giving Valdoro to the de Zurgas. It's infamous, but then so is everything about this marriage. And what will happen when I tell them I'm not going through with it? It will serve them right to have their precious plans smashed at the last moment.

There was only one consolation in the whole of that evening. Before Elena went to her room she slipped into Maddalena's apartments and heard the late night news. The bulletin on Gregor's health was more detailed than she had previously heard. It went into medical technicalities; a quantity of blood had collected inside the chest wall, causing the lung to collapse, and the need to aspirate it had been immediate. This having been done, the General's condition had begun to improve. He was responding to transfusions, and although still gravely ill was not considered to be at such a critical stage.

There's hope, thank God, Elena thought. There's hope.

CHAPTER TWELVE

The next day everything revolved around the forthcoming marriage. Don Pablo, who normally used his telephone at home as little as possible, made a series of calls to spread the good news through the family circle, and arranged a dinner party for that evening. In the morning they all went to Mass. After that, there was business to be settled, and for this purpose Doña Luisa was soon closeted with Don Pablo in his study. Carlos was included; but not Elena.

In the afternoon the guests arrived.

Most families have some elderly unattached relative. more or less infirm, who having no close ties need participation in family affairs as much as food and shelter. The de Zurgas had Doña Caridad, a tottery old lady in her seventies. She had plenty of money, and it was her habit to travel around, staying with various members of the family for a month or two at a time, and in that way to keep a fairly accurate finger on the collective de Zurga pulse. Her body was ageing but her mind was as acute as ever, and she had the de Zurga liking for arousing any sleeping dogs she came across. As she had recently billeted herself on Manuel, Carlos's brother, it was inevitable that she should appear for the celebration dinner.

Doña Ana arrived almost simultaneously with Manuel's party, so Elena had no chance for a private word with her. As they kissed Doña Ana whispered: 'Why?'

The look she gave Elena was troubled as well as questioning, but Elena could only give a small shake of the head; even if she had the opportunity she was not free to speak.

'Well, you're a lucky girl!' Doña Caridad shouted in a cracked treble. 'You've done well for yourself! He's a fine boy.

And a rich one, too!'

Elena kissed the sallow wrinkled cheek. 'Hello, Aunt Caridad.'

'What's your dowry, my dear? It's all settled, I suppose?'

'I haven't got a dowry, Aunt Caridad,' Elena said, loudly and clearly, with a vengeful pleasure.

'*What*? *No dowry*! Every girl should have a dowry, for her own self-respect! What's Luisa thinking of? She's not penniless yet!'

'I'd take Elena without a dowry any time, Aunt Caridad,' interposed Carlos smoothly.

'And so you should, you little Croesus!' she chuckled.

'It appears I'm taking the promise of Valdoro, which even in its reduced state should be good enough for the de Zurgas,' Elena announced.

Doña Ana gave her a quick glance. She thinks that's why I'm marrying him, Elena thought. It will do until I'm able to tell her the truth.

'Oh, oh! You're not doing so badly, Carlos! Valdoro and a lovely girl. But you'll have to watch her tongue, it's sharp!' Doña Caridad gave a travesty of a giggle.

Carlos took Elena's arm and leaned close to her. 'She'll only say sweet things to me. Isn't that so, *querida*?'

Elena forced a smile. Manuel came up to them.

'Congratulations, Carlos! So you've persuaded her! Some time you must tell me how you managed it. Now I can claim a brotherly kiss.'

All afternoon Elena sought an opportunity to be alone with Doña Ana, and consistently the chance eluded her. What made it worse was the fact that it had already been decided she should not return to the Avenida de Mayo yet, but should stay with her mother for the convenience of making the wedding arrangements and fitting her trousseau.

Carlos had expected her to leave her post at Agricultural Chemicals at once — an odd idea for a business man — but she had carried her point that she must work out a week's notice. He had countered by saying that he or Doña Luisa would meet her in the lunch hour so that no time need be wasted. His intentions were transparent. He was not going to give her any opportunity to go to the hospital. She could have wept with frustration.

At last came the celebration dinner. A more ghastly affair, Elena thought, could hardly have been imagined. Clinging to the knowledge that she was not going through with the wedding she ought to have seen a certain ironic humour in it, but even that was beyond her. She was embarrassed beyond belief.

In the circumstances the outcome could have been foreseen. During the meal the talk was much of marriage; this led to joking and veiled innuendoes which, instead of being dropped, were tossed to and fro and elaborated to the point of ribaldry.

Elena, scarlet with embarrassment, gazed at her wine-glass and gritted her teeth. Every hour seemed to make matters worse. Up to this morning she had given Carlos the benefit of the doubt, had accepted that his accusations of Marint had been made from a standpoint of family pride and decent behaviour.

But now she saw that he himself lived according to the de Zurga rules, which were not 'Live honourably, do no sin', but 'Be as dishonourable as you please, sin as much as you wish, as long as you do not make it public.'

She could not bear to look at the faces of the men around the table. They knew Carlos's true colours, and saw nothing wrong. The prospect of his taking her to wife aroused no compassion for her in their minds; she knew they were looking at her, considering his future delight in her body with amusement and envy. There was covetousness in Manuel's admiring glance; next to her Enrique from under lowered eyelids was sidelong making a catalogue of her attractions; even Don Pablo, having had his day and finding that vigour was now often overruled by indolence, was resenting giving up his position as leader of the herd, and was jealous of his son's fresh opportunity to demonstrate his manhood. They were all

177

no better than rutting animals.

She longed to rush to a window and fling it open; the room was stuffy, the whole house was oppressive, it smelt of lechery and decadence.

Don Pablo decided it was time for him to make a speech; he began with a string of ponderous and hackneyed phrases about a 'longed-for alliance', 'a marriage dear to my heart', 'an ardent bridegroom and a lovely bride', and went on and on until Elena was ready to scream.

On a flood of fatherly advice Don Pablo came to an end. Doña Luisa requested a speech from Carlos in reply.

'Really, now, you can't expect *me* to make a speech!' he protested suavely. 'You all know how delighted I am – there's nothing more to say.'

'Then kiss the bride-to-be and have done with it,' drawled Manuel.

'With the greatest of pleasure.'

Carlos pushed his chair back and took Elena by the hand. She resisted and began to protest. To have Carlos showing his ownership by kissing her . . .

'*Hombre!* You'd better assert yourself.' Don Pablo gave a lewd chuckle. 'She's yours. Start as you mean to go on.'

Carlos's hand was tight round hers. He was dragging her to her feet. She must either struggle with him or give in.

'Elena is only being girlish and shy,' he said smoothly. 'We agree very well about everything.'

She knew what he meant, and did not dare to defy him. She stood meekly at the foot of the table.

He put his arms round her and set his mouth on hers in a kiss of practised sensuality, prolonging the intimacy, holding her body close to him. His breath was heavy with wine and garlic, his lips disgustingly moist. His right hand which was out of the general view moved round from her waist, round and up until it rested on the side of her bosom, the fingers splayed about her ribs, creeping into her bare armpit, the palm pressing and lifting the breast as his mouth played on hers.

She raised one foot. The heel of her shoe was high and thin;

178

she set the point of it on his instep and leaned all her weight upon it.

Quite hurriedly he released her.

The Thunderbird roared down the drive and out on to the main road. Carlos stole a sideways glance at Elena. She was presenting him her profile, lovely and impassive, looking down, her eyelashes dark fringes above the petal-pale curve of her cheek. How should he speak to her? To say he regretted his behaviour of the previous evening would not be true; but he realized it had been ill-advised. He could not, even under such odd circumstances, have expected Elena to take it without some retaliation. She had spirit, and he had never objected to that in a woman. His foot was still damned sore.

The trouble was, he admitted to himself, he had been not only tipsy with wine, but drunk with power. His father had begun to have doubts, his brothers were more or less openly sceptical about his chances of marrying Elena — but here he was, never mind how he'd managed it, officially engaged. There had been a certain amount of drinking to his success, it wasn't surprising that wine and a sense of achievement had loosened his self-restraint as well as clouding his judgment. Even now, with the celebrations put behind him, he still felt as he had done last night.

He was like an avid collector who had long coveted a particular *objet d'art*. Now at last it would be his, there was only the contract to be signed.

He reached down and took her hand. She flinched a little as if she expected him to caress her, but did not resist when he raised her fingers to his lips.

'Yesterday evening I was in too much of a hurry. I admit it,' he said magnanimously.

'I am glad to hear it!' she retorted indignantly, drawing her hand away. 'The agreement was that I will marry you. Not that you should be free to treat me like some back-street tart!'

So she was still on her high horse. He was faintly surprised that she even knew the word.

'There are plenty of respectable women who would not object to anything I did last night.'

'Then I suggest you marry one of them.'

So much for his attempts at being concilliatory. He'd know better than to bother another time.

'But I wish to marry *you*,' he replied coldly.

'I can't think why -- you don't love me in the slightest.'

'You think not? I hardly know myself.'

He took his eyes off the road for a moment and let his glance slide over her.

'Perhaps it is love to want you as I do. It is certainly reason enough for me. I want you, I must have you. Since you are -- who you are -- marriage is necessary.'

He had the satisfaction of seeing her cheeks flame. The meaning of his look had been as plain as his words. He hoped she felt stripped. He was going to leave her in no doubt of his intentions.

'We are going to marry as soon as possible. I am not a man who cares for his desires to be kept waiting.'

She was silent for so long that he thought she was not going to reply. Then she said bitterly, 'And you want Valdoro, don't you? You're getting it. I should have thought that would have been enough for you.'

He smiled. 'Oh, no. That is merely what is called, I believe a "fringe benefit". Now, to practical matters. Today I will arrange for our engagement to be announced, and also see if we can choose a ring. And for the sort of ring I shall buy, the jeweller will see us in his private office when the shop is closed. I don't buy that kind of thing over the counter · nor would he wish to sell in that way.'

He intended her to be impressed. He did not want to push her too far, and it would do no harm to show her he was prepared to give her material advantages most women would envy.

'As my wife, you will have a leading position in our social set,' he remarked. 'I shall see that you can more than hold your own as far as clothes and jewels are concerned.'

'I have jewels. My father was very generous to me. And what makes you think I shall want to mix with your social set?'

Her coldness provoked him.

'What you want hardly enters into it. You will be expected to do your duty as a wife and hostess. The de Zurgas need such a person. Concha is out of town too much, and Maddalena is too lazy, besides which I am the eldest son, so my wife will take precedence. I assure you, you will have a good establishment. Most women enjoy that.'

'I know I'm selling myself. You needn't rub it in.'

Now he was satisfied. She had shown him he had struck home.

'Not at all. It is nothing so crude. We have made a civilized agreement, which is to the benefit of both of us. Not forgetting a third party, of course.'

'No, I shall not forget that.'

Damn her! Damn her for caring about Marint! Just let them be married — he'd knock the nonsense out of her

All the way to Police Headquarters Elena had been wondering why she had been called by the Varena Chief of Police to see him. There had been no question of compulsion, but it was not a request one could refuse.

As she entered the building the whole of Police Headquarters seemed to be humming with quiet activity. She was escorted politely but firmly upstairs, and after a brief wait in an outer office she was shown into an inner sanctum and the door closed behind her. She was alone with the Chief of Police.

The most handsome man she had ever seen got up from the desk and placed a chair for her. He stood by her chair until she was seated and then resumed his place.

He began to speak, and from his tone they might have been at a dinner party. His manner, his address, all had terrific style. This interview promised to be more of a social event than an interrogation. Suddenly she felt at ease; the last thing she had expected was to find an aristocrat, one of her own kind. But this he undoubtedly was. She need have no qualms about how she would be treated.

'You have guessed, of course, why I wish to talk to you?'

For one hysterical moment Elena thought: Yes. Carlos has delusions of grandeur and has asked you to control the crowds at the wedding. Then she pulled herself together.

'No. I have no idea.'

The reply jolted her back to reality. 'But naturally, about the unfortunate accident to General Marint.' The fine eyebrows had arched slightly, his voice was well-modulated, he spoke with beautiful precision.

'I don't want you to think this is a police enquiry,' he was quick to reassure her. 'It is simply that there are one or two points which are not clear to me; I want to know them purely for my own satisfaction.'

She looked at him questioningly.

'You see, the matter is not as straightforward as it appears. There are three aspects to the case. First, there is General Marint's account of what happened. Second, there is the version as told to the Press and the public of what happened - for which I was responsible. Third, there is what really happened. That is the aspect which interests me.'

At last she felt the authority under the smooth manner. Completely at a loss she stared at him in silence. He returned to her a bland and sympathetic gaze.

'I expect you would like to know the General's version. He dictated and signed a statement in which he says he shot himself - by accident.'

'But that's fantastic!'

'Quite fantastic. Anyone would see that. Gregor Marint has been a professional soldier for a number of years, weapons are the tools of his trade, he has a healthy respect for them and handles them correctly by habit. Then why should he make such a statement? For two reasons. To satisfy the doctors who would see the nature of his wound, and to show me that he did not want any sort of enquiry made should he die before he

182

had the chance to speak to me.'

Horror and fear gripped her. 'But — he's not going to die?'

'Please don't distress yourself. It seems unlikely now. So — we know he could not have shot himself by accident. If proof is needed I have that too. As soon as I heard what had happened I went to the hospital. There I examined the General's coat for powder burns. The absence of such marks showed me that the gun had been fired at a distance well over arm's length. No, he didn't shoot himself.'

Colonel Córdoba leaned back in his chair and continued in his friendly, confidential manner.

'So I asked myself how, why, and by whom was he shot? I can tell you now that one circumstance has helped me considerably — the weapon.'

She could not help giving him a quick and curious look.

'In our country there is plenty of choice. Quite apart from regular military weapons, there is, in private possession, in spite of the calling-in of firearms, a large number of rifles and shotguns of assorted makes and ages, pistols and revolvers, and I dare say a fair sprinkling of useable antiques. Incidentally,' he chatted away, 'did you know that Gregor Marint is an expert, internationally acknowledged, on antique firearms?'

She shook her head.

'But I don't suppose it would interest you. Would you even know, for instance, an antique duelling pistol if you saw one?'

'I think so. We have a pair at home.'

'Indeed? At Valdoro?'

'Yes. They are family heirlooms.'

'Then it was almost certainly one of that pair which someone fired at the General.'

He had calmly dug a pit and she had fallen in. Or was she imagining it? It was impossible to tell. He went on as pleasantly as ever. 'Perhaps you would like to see the General's statement?'

From under the sheaf of papers he drew a folded sheet, rather crumpled, with brown stains along one side. She opened it delicately and read.

183

'... It says, at Valdoro House, but the papers say it happened at the State Farm!'

'Ah, yes, but if you remember,' he reminded her gently, 'the papers printed my version. Gregor Marint couldn't say that. There would be no antique pistols at the State Farm, and he had to admit to the weapon because of the nature of the wound.'

She felt very obtuse as the Colonel continued to expound to her as if he would be happy to do so for the rest of his life.

'Have you ever seen a wound caused by a modern bullet?'

'A few times.'

'Then you will know it makes a fairly small neat hole. Our doctors have had plenty of experience of gunshot wounds; none of them would confuse such a one with the results of a ball from an old duelling pistol.' He paused. 'That is a much more unpleasant sight. Quite a large entry hole. But Gregor Marint had as well an exit hole in his back which was considerably bigger, with bits of splintered shoulder-blade in it and great lumps of shredded flesh hanging down around it. Have you seen such a wound? It's not pretty.'

She shook her head, flinching at the thought. Ideas were forming in her head. She tried to push them out but they turned round and round like squirrels in a cage as the Colonel went on talking.

'But I think you have.'

The voice was as smooth as silk, as smooth as polished steel, probing into her.

'Gregor Marint sequestered your land, but that was a matter of Ministry business. It wasn't personal. You must know he's nothing like as black as he's been painted. In fact, he's a very good fellow when one knows how to handle him. Did he anger you, or make you jealous? What was it? Señorita Moural, in heaven's name, *what possessed you to shoot him*?'

She stared at him dumbfounded. Then she could only stammer, 'I? *I* — you think that *I* shot him?'

His eyes were cold and clear. 'Didn't you?'

'No!' She pulled herself together. 'And if you had made the

simplest enquiry you would have found that I haven't been near Valdoro for weeks. I couldn't possibly have shot him.'

He took it very calmly. 'In that case, I apologize. You see, Gregor Marint is a close personal friend of mine, and he persuaded me to promise him that, if he lived and suffered no permanent injury, I would not pursue any enquiries. But I have my professional pride. I have to know what happened. I have been doing it all here,' — he touched his desk — 'and here.' His fingers brushed his forehead. 'Very well. I will go back over my reasoning and you shall tell me where I went wrong.'

Oh, no! she thought. Leave it. I don't want to know any more.

But Colonel Córdoba's large eyes narrowed thoughtfully. 'Let us follow my original line of thought in greater detail. If someone had planned to shoot General Marint — to murder him — they would not have chosen that weapon, time, or place. I have no doubt your *vaqueros* carry guns as a necessary part of their equipment on the pampa?'

She nodded.

'Then there would have been guns in the bunkhouse. It was the day of your bloodstock sale, the place was thronged with people, that would have been the time and place, not later when everyone had left. When the crowds were there detection would have been difficult and escape easy. No, it wasn't an ordinary murder attempt.'

He was dispassionate, analytical. She began to suspect his quality.

'What then?'

Once more the ideas she had been fighting to dispel invaded her mind.

'I know it was committed in your house, in the main hall I believe with one of a pair of pistols which normally hang on the chimney-breast. Now an intruder would bring his own weapon, even if he merely came to rob. The pistol was loaded and fired by someone familiar with it — that is, either one of the servants or a member of the family.'

185

His eyes had lost their soft melting expression long ago. They were shrewd and clear, calculating; they were weighing her up, and with a jolting shock she realized she had completely underestimated him. He was no socialite playing detective. He was clever, complex, and a consummate actor. She knew she must watch every word she said, and she guessed it was already too late. And she still did not know what he was trying to prove.

He pressed the bell on his desk. A sergeant entered.

'Some coffee, Sergeant.'

He turned to her again.

'I'm afraid all this is rather distressing for you. I am so sorry. That is the worst of my job. I sometimes have to bring the hard facts home to the nicest of people. Now where were we?

'Oh, yes, the servants. Well, it could hardly be one of them – they would be more likely to idolize the General than want to injure him, and any one of them who had a motive – a grudge – would have plenty of opportunity to borrow a *vaquero's* gun and use it – behind one of the outbuildings, for instance – why should they take such an awkward thing to load as your pistol, and fire at him indoors? No, whether planned or not, it had to be one of the family.'

She felt icy cold; her brain simply refused to work, she was hanging on his words, waiting for him to tell her what she could not bring herself to believe.

'Now there are three of you, and you, I thought, would be the most likely one. The most charming girls, in my experience, are capable of quite extraordinary actions when roused into a passion. But then, you say you were not there.'

He put the paper-knife neatly on the desk, and straightened his papers. 'So. It was your mother.'

Was it two minutes – three minutes – she sat there, silence filling the room; the pause seemed interminable? Colonel Córdoba was content to say nothing, and she could not speak. It couldn't be true!

She knew her mother was impulsive yet calculating,

186

passionate, arrogant, that she hated Gregor Marint — but deliberately to load the old Moural pistol and to shoot him down! No, it wasn't possible. There could be no explanation for it.

'I can't believe it,' she whispered. 'She couldn't do such a thing.'

'I believe she could — and did.' His voice, cool and steady, answered her. 'I have a little more to tell you. I have seen Gregor Marint this morning — '

'How is he?' she asked urgently. 'Everything will be all right?'

'If not, would it be partly your fault?'

'No! I've told you I didn't do it, and I know nothing.'

'There must be some reason. You should know — '

'But I don't! *How is he?*'

'He had a good night, and is much improved this morning. In fact — ' he smiled — 'when I saw him he had just been shaved. He remarked he considered it had been done by the undertaker's assistant, as that is the only person he knows to shave a man who is lying down. "And that is as much as he is doing for me this time," he said, "he can go away and practise on somebody else." '

She began to laugh. She found it hard to stop. She was shaking. *Dios*, I mustn't lose control here. What's the matter with me? she thought.

The sergeant came in and put a tray on the desk. Colonel Córdoba nodded and waved him away.

'Sugar and cream?' He was pouring the coffee.

'Do you smoke? No, I thought not. He is out of danger, Señorita Moural. I apologize for not telling you before.'

'Thank you.'

He waited while she drank her coffee. Then: 'I was unkind to you, and no doubt Gregor will be furious. But I had to know. I never close a file without satisfying myself that I have the truth of a case. And you must face the fact that your mother was responsible. I told you that Gregor asked me to make no enquiries. He said that, if I did, it would cause a

187

scandal to a young lady — a scandal which would be completely unjustified. So, as he is surviving satisfactorily, I have not proceeded with a charge, but I had to work the case out for myself nevertheless.'

'He said that?'

'Yes. I have talked to the aide who was with him, though not in the room at the time. He supports the written statement absolutely — that Gregor shot himself. He is doing it from loyalty to the General, of course. But he supported him rather too well. He told me it must be so, because when he entered the hall directly after the shot the only people there were the General and Señora Moural. I admit I thought he was covering for you.'

'And Gregor made that statement — to protect my mother — '

'No, Señorita Moural, I think not. To protect you.'

'*Me*?'

'Of course. Remember the reason he gave me. If I may be allowed to say so, you are young — and beautiful. If it were known that your mother had shot the General, people would draw a certain conclusion, and your reputation would suffer. Not hers — she would play the rôle of the avenging parent. What puzzles me is — since she did not have that reason, why did she do it?'

She gazed at him for a long moment. Of course he was right.

'I don't know — it's all so awful — I can't think. What will you do?'

'See her, talk to her, tell her she is lucky I am not arresting her on a charge of attempted murder — or malicious wounding, at best. But I wish I knew *why*. I must know. Was it just a moment of anger, or having failed once to kill him, will she want to try again? I cannot risk that.'

In her worst moments Elena had not thought of that.

'Don't worry, Señorita Moural, I shall find out. And I shall make sure there is no danger of repetition.'

188

Elena would never know how she managed to return to her office, to continue with her work and wait calmly until Carlos came to take her to lunch.

The truth about Gregor's wounding and Carlos's blackmail had acted as a catalyst on her, causing her emotions and her problems to cohere and produce a plan of action. Carlos was so heartless, so selfish, he deserved a little of his own medicine, and she was now in the mood to give it. If she could, she would have punished her mother too. It was worse than Carlos's treatment to find that her own mother had been the one to injure, almost to kill, the man she loved. She must fight them both as best she could; and that meant they must believe she had accepted the inevitability of the marriage, while she cast about to find means of coming at the truth of Gregor's visits to the Via Colón.

Carlos had told her she would have jewels and an establishment most women would envy; very well, now he was going to back up his words. The ring would be a very good start.

An hour later they were lunching in Carlos's favourite restaurant, and the ring was on Elena's finger. Lorca's entire stock of expensive rings — and Lorca's rings were very expensive — had been brought out for her inspection in an office which was like a drawing-room at the rear of the luxurious shop. Señor Lorca himself had attended to them, and given them red-carpet treatment.

The ring Elena chose was not one she normally would have wanted, but if Carlos was to be taught his lesson it might as well be with something she could bring herself to relinquish later on. Until then she had not cared greatly for diamond solitaires, but now she admitted to herself, although she could hardly lift her fork, this one had some advantages. It had set Carlos back for a great deal of money, and it must have increased his respect for her acumen.

To her great surprise he had rallied from the shock to his bank balance, and was in a better temper than he had been for some while. It was fantastic, but the choice of such a fabulously expensive ring had in some odd way given him considerable gratification. Perhaps he thought she would not have had the nerve to choose it if she did not intend to keep her word and marry him.

As the meal proceeded she decided it must be so. He thought she had thrown up the sponge, was giving in to him completely, and had settled to make the best of a bad job and get as much out of it as she could.

They had little time for private conversation. The restaurant seemed to be almost exclusively frequented by acquaintances of Carlos, mostly male. Young men came up to their table in little processions like wasps to a honey-jar, were introduced, were told about the engagement, and invariably professed their desolation that Elena should be snapped up before her re-introduction to society. It is difficult to ignore a diamond the size of a small decanter-stopper, and Elena kept it well in view, while Carlos lost no opportunity to take her hand in his and show it off. So Elena's ring was much admired, and Elena herself by implication, the young men casting subtle compliments and not-so-subtle glances which ranged from longing to lechery. She endured it all with a smile, although the ring became more like a fetter every minute.

Carlos was basking in pride of possession and the warmth of his generosity; but the more he was known to have lavished on her the worse would be his humiliation when he was jilted. She hugged the thought to herself and endured the ogling of his friends with perfect composure.

CHAPTER THIRTEEN

Colonel Córdoba, formerly Don Ramón Miguel José Luis de Córdoba y Quirito, ended his interview with Señora Moural, formerly the Condesa de Valdoro, and left the de Zurga mansion with his usual air of calm assurance. He felt considerably less comfortable than he looked; not because the ex-Condesa had made it clear that she considered him a traitor to his family and to society, but because he was wondering what on earth he was going to say to Gregor Marint.

Ramón Córdoba knew full well that although he had in his official capacity emerged the victor from his passage of arms with the señora, she had nevertheless struck some very shrewd blows at him in his unofficial rôle as Gregor's friend. Ninety-nine women out of a hundred, when directly accused of the shooting, would have denied it and spent the next hour protesting their innocence; when worn down and completely cornered, they would have spent another half-hour arguing that they were justified. Señora Moural, when challenged, simply looked him in the eyes and said scornfully, 'That, no doubt, is the General's story.'

The ball, to change the metaphor, was in his court.

'On the contrary, Señora, the General's story is that he shot himself by accident. I can prove that to be impossible, and I know he told me that tale to prevent a police enquiry in public which would end in a scandal.'

'I quite understand that. The General has already had more than enough scandal to last him a lifetime.'

One had to admire her nerve.

'The General, Señora, is too great a man to care what is gossiped about him. But he does care for your daughter's reputation — more than you do, it seems.'

191

Anyone who did not know the facts would say she was stung to a righteous fury.

'My daughter's reputation! He has done his best to ruin it!' Córdoba's eyebrows lifted, but before he could say anything she continued. 'They were seen together on a public occasion, she was unchaperoned, and what was more, the whole thing was commented on in the newspapers. It is most fortunate that her cousin is tolerant and affectionate enough to overlook it. Most men of our class would have withdrawn their offer of marriage when they read that report in the *Noticia*!'

Tolerant and affectionate! He would not have applied either of those epithets to Carlos de Zurga.

'I think you know what I mean. Let's not beat about the bush, Señora Moural. You shot the General, and I can prove it. If that were to come out your daughter's name would suffer. I cannot allow myself to be swayed by that, but there are other considerations. If – and I say *if* – I take no action now – by the General's request – I must know that there will be no repetition of the offence.'

'If you wish to proceed with this ridiculous charge I cannot stop you. But I must say that I am surprised your new associations could so warp your principles of behaviour that you are prepared to persecute a widow and pillory her innocent daughter.'

He was forced to a grudging admiration. She was quite an actress. But it was playing outside the rules to imply that, on breaking with the hidalgo tradition into which he had been born, he had renounced all decent standards of conduct. What was more, she had given him no answer.

'Señora Moural, do you wish to stand trial on a charge of malicious wounding – attempted murder, even?'

She paused a moment, taking it quite calmly.

'No. But neither, I imagine, would General Marint wish to give evidence if there should be a trial.'

It had been quite a job cracking her, and he hadn't enjoyed it. But he had to find out her motive for the shooting, and when it did emerge as less than murder he was infinitely relieved. He let himself appear to be satisfied with her explanation, gave her a lecture with the full weight of his authority behind it, and told her not to rely on the case being hushed up.

In his car on the way back to Headquarters he digested what he had been told. The General had been interfering in her affairs, and her daughter was unduly influenced by his opinions. She had arranged a very suitable marriage to which her daughter had given her consent; the General had threatened to upset it by advising against it and on the spur of the moment she had taken the only way she knew to prevent him from seeing her daughter.

It had been rash and wrong of her, but she was trying to safeguard her family's interests. She was a widow, deprived (he was sure she substituted that word for 'robbed' at the last minute) of money and land, it was vitally important to her to provide for her daughter's future.

She may have been lying in part, but she did it very convincingly. If he told Gregor her version, Gregor might think it desirable to tell him the truth. But to tell Gregor at this stage that the marriage was settled, that Elena had agreed, was a chancy business. There was no knowing what reaction it might provoke, but it would certainly not be good for Gregor's health — or his associates' comfort.

To make matters worse, de Zurga had said the announcement would be in tomorrow's papers, and in hospital Gregor Marint might have enough spare time to get around to the announcement columns, which were not normally within the scope of his interest. So he might know in any case.

He leaned forward and spoke to the driver. 'Any calls other than routine, Sergeant?'

'No, sir.'

'Straight to Headquarters, then.'

He would not visit Gregor until tomorrow morning.

Rosa was waiting when Elena returned to the office, having given her ring back to Carlos for safe keeping. Another

193

gentleman came asking for you. I wrote his name down — let's see — yes, Señor Vargas.'

'Oh? Oh yes, he's from the Land Ministry. Did he leave a message?'

'No. But he said he was sorry he'd missed you.'

'Thank you, Rosa.'

She sat down at her desk and mechanically prepared for work, her mind on Vicente. Why should he call? It must be something important. But she could think of no reason, unless . . . what had Colonel Córdoba said? Something about the shooting, yes, that had stuck in her mind. ' . . . his side, who was with him . . . supported the statement . . . out of loyalty to the General . . . '

If the aide had been Vicente, what then? He had every reason to hate her mother, but she knew he would support Gregor's tale for her sake alone if he guessed her mother to be responsible. And naturally he would want to see her. And she wanted to see him, not about the shooting but because he was the only person who might possibly know something about the woman in the Via Colón.

She rang the Ministry, and was put through to Vicente's office. The girl who answered tried to be helpful.

'Señor Vargas? I'm so sorry, you've missed him. He has some business in the country.'

'Can you tell me when you expect him back?'

'Some time early next week, I think.'

'I see. When he comes back, will you please tell him Señorita Moural rang?'

'Yes, Señorita, I'll make a note of it.'

She could only hope that Vicente would realize that she wanted to see him and that it was urgent. She could not leave a more detailed message. As it was he might be embarrassed, but he could make the excuse she had rung about Valdoro. But if he didn't return before next week — a sense of sickening frustration welled up within her.

Next week would be too late, for by that time she would have left the office, she would be the whole while under her mother's or Carlos's eye – she would not be able even to get to a telephone where she could talk privately. If Vicente came to the house, which was most unlikely, she would not be allowed to see him alone. She would not have the remotest chance of asking him about the Via Colón. And visiting Gregor would be out of the question, Carlos would prevent that.

If the General was having a relapse he wasn't being very quiet about it. He didn't even have the decency to look pale and interesting, Ramón Córdoba thought as he entered the private ward; dark and devilish would describe his aspect far better. He hardly gave Ramón time to sit down before he started brandishing the morning's *Noticia* and airing his opinions.

'There's no sense in it, Ramón! She doesn't love him, and she doesn't want to marry him. So *why*? They've told her a fancy story about me, I'm sure of it, though that wouldn't have any bearing – and then she didn't believe it, she said it was nothing – and it *was* nothing, she's too level-headed.'

'No girl in love is level-headed.'

'In love – with whom?'

'You, of course.'

'*Hombre*! That's ridiculous. I'm just a rough soldier to her! But she detests de Zurga, so why?'

'Pique, perhaps?'

'*Pique*! She'd want a stronger reason than that I should hope. You've seen de Zurga. *Dios,* that's why I feel – well, you know what he is. I wouldn't trust him with a baby's rattle – but with Elena – ' He choked on his words, and within the limits of bandages and brace, tossed on his pillows.

'Don't excite yourself, there's a good fellow. When you're out of hospital – '

'*What*! Am I to lie here like some old sick grandmother? And she promised me – '

'To marry you?' *Dios*, this was serious!

'No, you fool. She promised not to marry de Zurga. I was feeling pretty queer at the time, but I know she did – was that why, because she thought I was dying? Would she have

195

promised anything?'

'Now, Gregor, there's no need to champ at the bit like this!' He was flushed, he really ought to settle down. 'I know it says the marriage will shortly take place, but consider what the family is like. They'll have an elaborate church wedding, and that can't be arranged in five minutes. In a few weeks you'll be out of here, long before anything is settled — '

'A few *weeks*! If you think I'm staying here — look, Ramón, it doesn't make sense. Why should she tell me she wouldn't marry him, and then break her promise? She's a girl who would consider her word almost as sacred as the Bible. Unless, of course, they're coercing her, but I can't see that it's possible. She's not dependent on her mother, she can earn her own living, and she has her aunt, Señora Carvelo, to turn to. Give me a cigarette, Ramón. In that drawer.'

'*Hombre*, have a cigarillo instead of one of those.'

He let Córdoba light a cigarillo for him, then lay back with it between his teeth, thinking. At length: 'You think it will be a few weeks yet?'

'But of course. They wouldn't consider it a proper marriage with a civil ceremony alone, and do you think the señora is the type to let her daughter marry quietly? No, it will be a big wedding, and that takes time. Long before that you will see her and find out what is going on.'

'I don't know.'

At last he looked at Córdoba, let go of the newspaper, took the cigarillo from his mouth and spoke quietly, yet with a sobering intensity.

'I shouldn't interfere. I've no right to her, Ramón, especially since I offended her . . . '

'She didn't look offended to me.'

'She's not one to bear a grudge. All the same, how do I know what she really wants? I'm not in her world.' His eyes narrowed, his mouth set bitterly. 'But I can't forget de Zurga. I've seen his eyes on her, and that was enough. You know what he is with women, and how he lives, with his flat in town for casual affairs, and his mistress in her apartment — and now he wants Elena! Even if I didn't care a *peso* for her the mere thought would disgust me. But hell and damnation, Elena! I *do* care! He's like a snake, he ought to be dealt with. It's tempting Providence to take a chance and do nothing for a few weeks. It's leaving the field clear for him, and he's not a clean fighter.'

'But what can you do here, if you don't see her? Now, wait, Gregor, and leave it to me. I'll arrange a meeting.'

'No. You say she knows how I got this.' He nodded at his shoulder. 'You are a meddler, Ramón! You shouldn't have let her know. But I suppose it was your professional conscience — never close a file without knowing the truth of the case. I've heard it before! But it complicates things between us, and with her mother's tittle-tattle it's hardly the time for a meeting, not while I'm stuck here. But somehow de Zurga must be discouraged — at least until I'm out of here and can conduct my own campaign.'

'Do you want me to clap him in gaol? I'm afraid I've no grounds, though I could be a little unethical and stretch something . . . '

'I wouldn't dream of it, Ramón!' He was leaning back and smoking again, with the glimmer of a smile lightening his eyes and mouth. 'But there is something you can do for me. I think I have it.'

'What is it?'

'You must put through a couple of telephone calls for me. I need some information. And if I get the right answers there is something I can do. I think I might cramp de Zurga's style a little after all. *Madre de Dios* it's a good idea!'

By Friday morning Elena had still received no word from Vicente. Her anxiety had grown day by day, inaction was wearing her down, she could stand no more of it and rang Vicente's office. She was informed that he was not expected back until the following week.

A little seed of panic began to grow inside her. From tomorrow lunch-time she would virtually be Carlos's prisoner.

197

She would be unable to use the telephone or talk to anyone in private. The de Zurga house was effectually a prison to her. And if the wedding should be fixed to take place before Gregor had recovered she would have achieved nothing. He must be fit to defend himself.

If only she knew the charge was groundless, and could be proved to be so! Proof, that was the vital matter, otherwise the mud thrown would stick. In her heart of hearts she had been counting on Vicente to make some kind of discreet enquiries at the Via Colón. Now she could not even contact him.

She dared not write. Even a private letter to his office might be opened, and in it she must give him some idea why she needed help. She did not know his home address. Should she risk a letter to his parents' house? She did not even know for certain whether they still kept the leatherwork shop. For a second she felt weak as memories flooded to the surface, then she resolutely thrust them down. Today. She must think about today. No, even if she wrote to Vicente he could not come to her in time.

There was only one thing to do. She must go to the Via Colón herself. She must find Señora Mendoza, make some sort of snap judgment of the kind of woman she was, and warn her that her association with Gregor was likely to be misinterpreted.

What manner of reception she would get, heaven only knew, but no matter how distasteful the meeting it had to take place. And Carlos was calling for her. That meant she must get away from the office early on the pretext of shopping, and try to get back in time to catch him.

She took a taxi to the Via Colón. It dropped her outside the apartment block, and with a thudding heart she went up to Apartment 3.

One could generally tell a certain type of woman by her appearance — and if she looked like that, what was to be done? There must be some reason for Gregor's visits — she refused to consider them prompted by a sordid need for physical satisfaction — but if it appeared so on the surface, what could she do? She gritted her teeth and took a deep breath. She must at all costs be in command of herself.

There was no name on the door. She put her finger firmly on the bell-push. A muffled trill broke the silence. She waited, fighting the nervous nausea which rose in her throat. Nothing happened.

She pushed the bell again. Still no one came. She rang once more, a long demanding peal. And at last had to accept the fact that no one was there.

More disappointed than she cared to admit, Elena walked out from the cool of the hallway into the noise and heat of the Via Colón.

She must get a taxi to the office. She had not been away long. With luck she would be there before Carlos. Taxis kept sweeping past her outstretched hand, they were all taken. She must get one, and quickly. When would one of them stop for her?

A private car slowed silkily to a halt beside her. Her eyes were on the passing taxis and she paid no attention as the driver got out.

'Allow me to give you a lift, Elena.'

It was Carlos.

It was like a blow in the pit of the stomach. Some instinct of self-preservation made her cover up and continue playing the rôle she had chosen for herself as Carlos's *novia*.

'Oh, Carlos! You surprised me! How did you know I was here?'

'Where else would you be? I know you like shopping in the Plaza. I thought you might have gone to Casaviente's.'

'Yes, the curtain material. I wanted to check it.

He was leading her to the car. 'Is it satisfactory?'

'I still haven't quite made up my mind.'

'Then I'll help you to choose. We shall have much more time together next week.'

'Yes, that will be best.'

He was acting too. Why was he playing with her? Instead of challenging her about her action he was pretending ignorance, being pleasant and considerate. She didn't know what to make of it.

'You haven't forgotten we have guests to dinner tonight? Jorge Morillo is coming. He's a rather dull fellow, but good-hearted. We have hopes that he may make a match with Cristina.'

'Cristina? I didn't know — '

'Yes. She has decided she is tired of being single. And she realizes that people of experience can help her to find a suitable husband. Aunt Luisa approves of Don Jorge. The fact that he's a little older than Cristina is in some ways an advantage. She needs a steady man.'

How do you — or I — know what Cristina needs? This is extraordinary, it's going back a hundred years, she thought. But then, at times, she felt that her mother and the other de Zurgas were out of place in this century. They were throwbacks, at least in their attitudes to personal relationships.

They were slowing down at a traffic light. He gave her a long, sideways glance.

'It pleases me to see you making preparations. I feel that you are adjusting yourself to your mother's wishes. And to me.'

Somehow she forced the words out. 'I am trying to do so.'

'Then you will succeed. It's the right way to start a marriage.' He smiled, his hand went out and rested on her knee. All her muscles tensed. Why did he always want to touch her? But she forced herself not to pull away from the sensual inquisitive fingers which circled her kneecap and crept caressingly up her thigh. 'Intentions are so important. If you want to please me, I am sure we will both find — ' The lights changed, he took his hand away and put the car into gear ' — our married life delightfully satisfying.'

He searched her with another look. It was as bad as having his hands upon her.

Don Pablo de Zurga was in high good humour. At last everything was going as it should. Carlos would soon be married; Elena was a fine girl.

It was late on Saturday afternoon, and with unusual sociability the members of the family in residence were gathered in the patio, lounging in garden chairs, lazing away the hot hours before it was time to dress for dinner.

Carlos was being very affable . . . his temper had improved ever since he had bought Elena's ring . . . Don Pablo thought he'd never known a man enjoy spending so much money on a bauble before – naturally a young man such as Carlos liked spending money, especially on himself, but all that for a ring for his *novia* – he must be really in love with the girl! Still it was in the nature of an investment. And there he was now, sitting on the cane chair he had pulled up between the *chaises-longues* Luisa and Elena were occupying – ah, he was a handsome boy! What if he did run after the women? It was natural, they liked it, and he had enough sense not to land himself in trouble, and with Elena he would be different: why steal fruit when you live in an orchard?

Don Pablo, musing and dozing, was roused from his thoughts by the sight of his eldest son taking Elena's hand and kissing it in front of everyone, and by hearing him say, 'Querida, forgive me for not consulting you, but I have arranged everything. We can be married the day after tomorrow.'

It was like a thunderclap from a clear sky. Everyone exclaimed, 'The day after tomorrow!' 'This Monday!' 'Why didn't you warn us?' and gazed at the two of them.

Elena started back and snatched at her hand but Carlos retained it, and she stared at him in surprise which looked almost like panic. *Dios*! The girl wasn't frightened of the marriage-bed, surely?

'We can't!' she cried, then seemed to steady herself. I mean, nothing is ready.'

'It doesn't matter, *chiquita*.'

'But, Mother, my trousseau – ' She had turned appealingly to Luisa.

'There's no need to get excited, my dear.' Luisa was taking

it very calmly. 'This is not the church wedding. Carlos has merely arranged the civil ceremony for Monday. None of our other plans are affected.'

'But why?'

'There was a difficulty over fixing it for the same day as the church wedding.' Luisa seemed to know all about it. 'You wouldn't want to interrupt your honeymoon to come back for it, would you? It was much simpler to fit it in earlier, and this Monday there happened to be time free.'

Now Carlos was trying to soothe her. 'I am so sorry, *chiquita,* I didn't have the chance to consult you. I thought I had better book that time rather than lose it. You do understand?'

Elena looked from her mother to Carlos and back again.

'I would much rather have waited until the church ceremony -- it doesn't seem right.'

So that was the trouble! What a religious miss she was! Don Pablo began to laugh.

'Carlos!' he boomed. 'Stop frightening your little sweetheart! Can't you see she's in spiritual torment? She wants a blessing first, and she thinks you're getting too impatient!'

Elena began to blush, but Carlos behaved like the man of the world he was.

'Of course I'm impatient.' He kissed her hand again. 'Who wouldn't be, in my place? But I shall respect Elena's wishes.'

It was beginning to get dark, there was a general movement towards the house. Dinner was not for another two hours at least, but Carlos's bombshell was something to discuss in private, his real motive worth speculating on; the obvious reason was titillating enough, and there might be more to it than that. No one believed that there were so many marriages in Varena that it wasn't possible to fix the civil ceremony at any other time between now and the end of next month.

Elena moved as if to rise, but Carlos's hand closed over hers.

'Stay with me a few minutes.'

202

She sank back. Doña Luisa and Don Pablo were the last to go. She hoped they too would stay, but Don Pablo began to lever himself up, saying to her mother, 'Come along, Luisa. Let's leave the sweethearts, they want to talk together.'

For a moment Doña Luisa hesitated. Elena could read her mother's mind: she still thought it slightly improper for a girl to be alone with a man, even with her *novio*; but she rose to her feet and walked slowly into the house at Don Pablo's side.

Carlos's hand was tight over hers, clamping it to the chair arm, he turned and leaned towards her.

'You brought it on yourself, you know.'

She did not move or answer.

'As soon as I knew you had gone to the Via Colón I knew I had to prevent you breaking your word. You've only yourself to blame.'

Still no answer.

'You were unlucky, weren't you? Still, you weren't to know that the Mendoza woman had run off! Perhaps her protector found out she had been taking other men. Why are women like that so greedy? I wonder how much Marint paid her? And I suppose you would have bribed her to invent some innocent-sounding story to save Marint's face! I must say, you had a nerve to go there.'

At last she managed to speak. 'It wasn't that at all. I wasn't breaking our bargain. I only wanted to see her — to see what sort of a woman she was. I was jealous. Surely you understand — '

'Yes, I understand all about being jealous!'

His voice sank to a whisper, the heat of his hand made a burning spot on her flesh, but all the rest of her was cold.

'But I don't trust you. That's why you've got to make up your mind by Monday. I am going to marry you.'

'But why? Why, in spite of everything?'

'By "everything" I suppose you mean your dislike of me and your preference for Marint? I'll tell you why. I have so many reasons, you'll learn them in time. But since you're so proud I'll tell you something now.'

'*Proud*?'

'Yes. Too proud when we were youngsters to mix on equal terms. Too proud to consider me when our marriage was first proposed. Proud in a hundred looks and tones of voice ever since that time. But not too proud to take up with a dirty ranch-hand, a *vaquero*, a mixed-blood private soldier who climbed up from the ranks by treachery and murder – and now tries to lord it over *us*! And you, an hidalga!

'Now listen to this. For years my father has wanted me to marry. When he suggested I swallowed *my* pride and asked for you again I decided he ought to make it worth my while. Before I set foot inside Valdoro I arranged it, it was all in writing, signed and settled between us.'

'What was settled? What could be settled before I agreed?'

'A most satisfactory contract. He agreed, since you were his choice and I had no wish to marry at all, that on our wedding day he would make over to me a considerable sum of money and a number of shares which would give me complete control of one of our businesses. He has held the power and the purse-strings for far too long Now I shall have something of my own to handle without any interference. I decided I could put up with marriage, even if I couldn't choose the bride, if she brought me money and power.'

'No doubt that's in the de Zurga tradition.'

'I expected to be bored with you, and so at first I was. And then one day at Valdoro I seemed to see you for the first time.'

He began to stroke the side of her neck to her shoulder, then back, up and down, up and down. She lay very still, as if to resist would provoke him.

'I saw you, not as my proud cousin, but as a beautiful and very desirable woman. Suddenly I was eager, I was burning to marry you, not for the money but for yourself. I saw that the rest of the contract would not be a duty, but an exquisite pleasure.'

His fingers closed around her chin, holding her face close-turned to his. She was oppressed, borne down by the touch and sight and smell of him.

'The rest . . . ?' The words floated out against her will.

'I knew what my father wanted out of the marriage. Now you know too. You couldn't be here long and stay unaware of his ambition, his obsession. I was sure he would be prepared to pay for that, too.'

'*What do you mean*?'

His eyes stared down at her, hard and rapacious, but his voice was low and smooth.

'Everyone knows he wants a grandson. Neither Manuel nor Enrique has given him that, and he's getting very impatient. So he was more than willing to agree that, when we have a son he will make a settlement on the boy, and I shall have full control of the money until the child comes of age.

'You see, at first I thought it would be merely a duty to have heirs, so that he could pay for them, and I would find my pleasure elsewhere. But now it's different. I look at you, and at once I'm hungry, I'm thirsting to possess you.

'I bargained for a settlement for every boy   I wonder how many we shall have? I don't care. Better boys than girls, but can only think of you — as I want you. Naked — mine — only mine — always mine — your beauty mine. Whenever I choose . . . '

She was outraged, horrified and frightened, for his desire seemed touched with madness. 'You can't possibly think I'll marry you after telling me that!'

He began to stroke her neck again, the sensuous gesture exaggerated in contrast to the businesslike tone of his voice.

'I think you will — when you really consider the alternative. Don't forget Gregor Marint. I have already made arrangements about López's notebook. Now, if you marry me on Monday, a phone call from me will ensure the book and the copy are sent to me, and you shall have them. If the call is not made by a certain time they will be delivered to a person who will know exactly how to use them to cause the maximum damage.'

'I won't do it. Do what you like. It's not possible — '

'So? Don't you love him enough for that? You won't save

his career and his reputation? That's a pity, because either way you'll lose him. It's time you faced the facts. Up to now it has amused Marint, it's flattered his vanity to be seen with you, to have people guessing just what the relationship is between you. Don't delude yourself that he ever intended to marry you – that would be political suicide for him. But to let people think he has only to lift his finger and an hidalga will come running – that's fine!

'But once he's disgraced things will be different. He won't be a minister any more – he'll be lucky if he's still a general. And you – where will you be?

'There will be an announcement in the papers that our wedding will not take place. It will be quite easy for me to behave as if I'm gallantly taking the blame, while in actual fact *I* have broken it off. Then there will be doubts about your reputation – '

'No! That's fantastic! You're making something out of nothing.'

'Am I? I hope so. But people always do, and some will certainly link our broken engagement and Marint's injury. There will be plenty of gossip. You won't be able to hide yourself from it at Valdoro, because that will be sold. Your mother has disowned you once; she'll do it again. You'll have to live with your Aunt Ana as her poor relation, and you'll find precious few people who will want to receive you socially without either sneering at you or patronizing you.

'And what do you think Marint will do? Confirm another set of scandalous rumours by taking up with you again? Do you really think he'll try to patch over your two shabby names by marrying you? Or would you like him to brazen it out and turn you into his camp-follower instead? If you've any sense you'll see he'll do neither. He'll throw you off before you drag him down, then he'll try to pull himself up again by his bootstraps! Just think it over. You'd better settle for me.'

He stopped speaking. He still bent over her, a dark bulk, a menace, a hated creature whose malice and jealousy and lust were enveloping her, tying her in ever-tightening bonds. His hands were warm on her arms as he leaned over her, drawing his body close. She tried to rise and break away from him, but he pressed her back into the chair.

'Not yet, *chiquita*! I haven't finished. I want you, quite objectively, to consider our marriage. Of course, I shall enjoy mastering you, particularly at first. I am only human, and you've been aloof and held me off for so long. You'll have to learn to be submissive. Naturally I shall expect you to be a dutiful wife, to entertain my friends, go out with me when I ask you, and stay at home when I tell you to stay. You have made me so jealous that it will be some time before I feel I can let you come and go as you please. But I won't be overbearing. I shall be proud of my beautiful wife and I shall be glad to show you off on social occasions. You will still meet and mix with your own friends. I shan't even cause the slightest unpleasantness if we and Marint should happen to attend the same public function. You may exchange greetings with him, though I couldn't allow you to meet him alone or in private. But if you keep your bargain as my wife I won't be unreasonable.'

'So that's to be my future with you.'

'That, and bearing and bringing up our children. In return you will never want for money or comfort. You may spend as you please, furbish the house, hire your own servants, buy horses, supervise Valdoro, whatever you choose. You must see that, if you refuse me now, you'll never have another offer like this. You'll wreck your life and Marint's too, without a possibility of salvaging anything. Just think of that tonight — and tomorrow.'

Slowly, reluctantly his hands drew away. He stood up.

'Let us go indoors. I don't wish to scandalize your mother by keeping you out here in the dark any longer.'

CHAPTER FOURTEEN

It had been an appalling scene.

When Elena on the Monday morning in front of the assembled family had announced that she did not intend to marry Carlos, the vials of wrath had broken and poured upon her head.

Carlos, his father and her mother, each had been furious with her for their own reasons and had overwhelmed her with their recriminations. Doña Ana had tried ineffectively to stem the flow of their fury; Concha, Maddalena and Cristina had been silent but most interested spectators; Manuel, and even Enrique, had remonstrated; and Doña Caridad had sat, her hands folded upon an ebony stick, repeatedly squawking demands to be kept up to date with the course of the quarrel.

Then Elena had been goaded into revealing that she only consented to the marriage under duress, whereupon Carlos at first denied it and then began to insult both Marint and herself.

His remarks to Elena had become so offensive that the scene had culminated in his brother Manuel throwing a glass of wine in Carlos's face. Only the combined intervention of Don Pablo and Enrique had prevented a fight taking place between the two elder brothers there and then in the drawing-room.

As soon as she could be heard Doña Luisa disowned Elena for the second time, and this, she announced, was irrevocable. Doña Ana (who for several nights running had prayed on her knees that the marriage would not take place) was thankful for the opportunity to demonstrate her partisanship in public, and retorted that as Elena had always been as dear as a daughter to her, she would not want for a mother's love or a roof over her head while she, Doña Ana, lived.

At this point Elena was able to leave the family stew to seethe and bubble; she went upstairs to finish the packing she had more than half done in the intention of leaving that morning.

The maid came for her cases, and she followed downstairs to the hall where she found Doña Ana and Manuel waiting for her. The house had become oddly silent after all the commotion, but it was not the silence of peace; it was more like the brooding quiet which prevails between two phases of an earthquake.

Manuel came forward and took her hand. 'Elena, the family has treated you very badly, and I for one regret it. If there is anything I can do for you please let me know. Now let me take you both to the car. I'm sure you won't want to see anyone before you leave.'

'No, I don't least of all, Carlos.'

'Ah, it was strange about Carlos,' remarked Manuel with a wickedly thoughtful air, and Elena saw Doña Ana's lips trembling.

'What about Carlos?'

'You could say,' Manuel replied smoothly, 'that my elder brother has been translated. It was a most interesting process.' He handed them into the car. 'You must get Doña Ana to tell you about it. It will enliven the journey.' He shut the door. 'Goodbye — and good luck.'

I shall need it, Elena thought, as she gave him a wave and then sat back beside her aunt, feeling more kindly disposed towards Manuel than she had done for years.

'What did he mean about Carlos?'

'You didn't hear anything?' Doña Ana's mouth began to twitch again. 'He is in the Army now.'

'*What*!'

'You had just gone upstairs when a sergeant and a squad arrived. With Carlos's call-up papers. They wanted to draft him at once for his National Service. At first he and Pablo insisted there must be some mistake, but no, there was his name and all particulars in black and white on the form. Then they

209

pointed out that he had always been exempt, and the sergeant said well, he wasn't any more. Pablo demanded time to get his lawyer, who must have forgotten to make some application, but the sergeant said no, Carlos must come at once. By now Carlos was fuming, and beginning to get a little worried, though he didn't really believe it was happening. Pablo offered the sergeant wine, but he refused most politely, he couldn't take it on duty. All very correct.

'Then Carlos stopped blustering and tried to bribe him to hold it over for a day, he'd get his lawyer and call at the officers' quarters in the morning. That was a calamitous mistake! The sergeant most haughtily refused Carlos's money and told him it wouldn't do him any good to go to the officers' quarters either — he was being drafted here and now, and starting as everyone must nowadays — *as a private!*'

Elena's eyes and mouth rounded with astonished delight, she was hanging on Doña Ana's words. Her aunt covered her eyes with her hand, and wailed feebly.

'Oh, my dear, it was like a scene from a comedy! There was the sergeant, very stiff and correct; there was Pablo, bursting with indignation and impotence; and there was Carlos, simply rigid with horror. 'A *private!*'' he said. ''That's impossible. I can't mix with fellows like that, they're low, ill-bred, they're absolute roughnecks. Some of them may even be lousy — before I know what's happening I shall be infested myself!'' ''Oh, no Señor,'' said the sergeant with an absolutely straight face, ''we're very particular about cleanliness in the Army now. Every man on entry has a delousing bath followed by a medical examination. That's compulsory.'' If you could have seen Carlos's face when he realized what was waiting for him! Imagine! Carlos being deloused! When they took him away he was incoherent, practically foaming at the mouth!'

At last Doña Ana gave way and collapsed into her corner of the car, bubbling with helpless laughter. The thread of Elena's control snapped and she found herself joining in, laughing until she was on the verge of hysteria.

Doña Ana wiped her eyes. 'I must say it was a master-stroke

of Gregor Marint's!'

'Gregor? Why Gregor?'

'But of course it's his doing! He saw your engagement in the papers and determined to delay the wedding! Carlos can't marry you if he's confined to barracks as a new recruit! Oh, I'm sure it's all legally correct. Marint's too fly to do anything outside his rights. But why else should Carlos be called up after all these years? Imagine Carlos, living as a private and drilling with a squad! It has a touch of genius!'

'I can't believe it!'

'Well, I can! I really think I know your General better than you do!'

Doña Ana was still giggling like a girl when Elena remembered that the situation was basically unaltered; that Carlos had said that he would not lift a finger to prevent the scandal being spread, and by now his wretched plan in the absence of a phone call from him would be in its first stage. She must take the action on which she had decided.

'Aunt Ana, I must go to Police Headquarters at once.'

When Elena entered Colonel Córdoba's office everything looked as before, and the Colonel was as charming as ever. His soft dark eyes gazed into hers across the desk, he gave her an encouraging little smile and asked, 'Well, Señorita Moural, and how can I help you?'

All her careful introductory phrases left her.

'It's General Marint. I don't know what you can do, but there must be something - '

'Please explain. What is the trouble?'

'There's going to be a scandal,' she blurted out. 'He may be disgraced and ruined, unless you can stop it.'

The Colonel allowed himself to look mystified. 'What scandal? You must give me some details.'

'Colonel Córdoba, I am so ashamed to have to tell you this . . .' His eyebrows began to rise. 'It's my cousin he hates the General, and he's determined to discredit him.'

'Which cousin, señorita?'

211

'Carlos de Zurga. I don't know how to tell you – '

'Just give me the plain facts. Nothing shocks or surprises me. I have a professional immunity, you know.'

His smile was reassuring. She plunged into her account.

'My cousin had the General watched. He wanted to find a way of blackening his character. He discovered the General had been paying visits – to a young woman who lives alone. He is going to use this information to . . . to cause a scandal, hoping that if the General's character suffers enough the President will remove him from office . . . '

Colonel Córdoba considered her gravely. 'I see. Why didn't you tell me this before?'

'Before . . . ?'

'You have known it for some little time. Over a week.'

She gazed at him astounded. He leaned back.

'López couldn't quite fathom what your cousin was after,' he continued. She had no answer for this either. He went on: 'At first, when he was told to watch General Marint he was afraid someone might be studying his routine with a view to assassination. So he reported the matter to me. Obviously it was valuable to me for him to continue doing the job he'd been hired for, and to keep in touch with my department.

'General Marint's shooting accident really had López worried. But the General's movements outside Varena had not been within López's scope. Then the next day you were presented with his notebook; and he drew his own conclusions. He told me, and I drew mine. That's why I am asking, why did you not tell me before?'

She wished he would keep to the point, to the real reason for the interview.

'I couldn't. I tried to stop my cousin using the notebook. If I had told anybody he would have known.'

'But you have told me now.'

'Yes' she agreed desperate. 'Now I can't stop him any longer from making trouble. So you must.'

'If I can. What are his plans?'

'He says he has given the notes to someone who will know

how to use them. I am sure he intends them to be published. Colonel Córdoba, please, you *must* stop it.'

'Señorita, how can I? If I knew who had the book I should still be powerless at this stage. I can't forbid anyone to print anything they wish, I can only take action afterwards, if necessary. And you haven't told me yet what conclusions are to be drawn from this notebook.'

Dios, did he have to embarrass her like this? Couldn't he guess?

'My cousin is suggesting that — this Doña Raquel — she lives alone and receives men — that she is . . . '

'A prostitute? A spy? Or both?'

'The first,' she admitted. 'And he'll probably get round to the other.'

'If either is suggested in print, then I can take action.'

'But, Colonel, if someone prints it, and makes a scandal, the General is bound to suffer, whether it's true or not. I came to you because you're his friend — and surely you have the power to do something?'

'You came to me as the last resort, it seems!' He gave her a wry smile. 'You even tried to see Señora Mendoza — oh, I know about that too. Why leave it so late to tell me?'

How could she disclose to this man the wretched intimate details of Carlos's blackmail? Besides, it was all irrelevant now.

'Does it matter? Oh, I thought I could delay everything much longer.'

There was a tight look about the Colonel's mouth. 'I suppose he said that if you married him he would suppress it, and you played for time?'

At first Elena did not answer, but the look in her eyes must have given her away.

'Yes, I thought so. And today — '

There was a knock at the door, but it hardly registered with Elena.

'I thought I could give the General a chance . . . '

Her voice trailed away. She realized that a sergeant had entered the room and had at once stood aside in favour of

213

another man who came in unannounced, passed behind her chair and moved round to the desk. The sergeant placed a chair for him and he sat, a trifle clumsily, for his left arm was splinted and braced.

A wave of such emotion surged up within her that she could not look at his face, for if she did, she would betray herself.

She kept her eyes down. Don't think about loving him, think about anything else — of what he's wearing — brown shoes, fawn trousers. His shirt was cream coloured, with a string tie. The shirt sleeve had been slit to accommodate the arm dressings and strapped around them. His fawn jacket sat awkwardly over the thickness of the bandages on his shoulder and chest, and looked uncomfortable, the empty sleeve pinned across to the right front keeping it in place.

She wrote it all down in her mind, taking each detail in turn, struggling for composure, considering everything, even to the texture of the material of his suit.

His voice, with that distinctive resonance, was ringing cheerfully in her ears. 'Good morning. I hope I haven't missed anything?'

Her gaze had been fixed on his sleeve. Now she was ready.

She let her eyes be drawn up to his face, and her heart turned over at the sight of him. He was so close, she could see the creases which always appeared at the corners of his eyes when he smiled or narrowed them against the sun. He was smiling now.

His brown skin, no longer bloodless, had regained its healthy colour, the well-loved curve of cheek from high cheekbone to broad strong jaw was fractionally more hollowed. His mouth was strong, well shaped, his kisses wonderful . . . She saw his look flicker to her lips, caught the wild notion that he was thinking of kisses too.

No one had answered him yet. She must be rational.

'Gregor, I am so glad to see you so much better. I didn't know you were out of hospital.'

'I'm not.' He grinned. 'But I'm well enough to be let out on

214

parole this morning! – Thank you for your call, Ramón! I hate to be left out of anything that concerns me personally. Now who is going to tell me? What was so urgent?'

'Just a little plot of Don Carlos de Zurga's,' replied the Colonel pleasantly. 'Señorita Moural has set my mind at rest. I had thought that perhaps he intended to have you assassinated; it seems his aim is merely to disgrace and ruin you.'

'Is that all?' He grinned more broadly. 'He's not even original. That's been tried several times before. The same old methods, I suppose?'

He turned to Elena. 'And where is the gentleman? I thought he was your shadow nowadays? Have you given him the slip?'

Why can't they be serious? This isn't a joking matter, she thought.

'He's not here. He was called up for military service this morning.'

'How surprising, at his age!' was the bland reply. 'And he's hardly soldier material, I would say. His drill sergeant has my sympathy.'

There was so much she had to say, why couldn't she say it?

'Gregor – I know how you were injured. It was a dreadful thing to do. I am so sorry.'

'It's past history, and nothing to do with you. Don't apologize!'

'I must. And you protected my mother – for my sake –'

'Please! I was only being practical. It's all over.'

He turned to Córdoba. 'Is everything under control, Ramón?'

'More or less. We have to wait for the first move from de Zurga. You can help me in one little matter.'

'What's that?'

'Just tell me – who, or what, is Señora Mendoza? No one seems to know, and I thought it might be tactless at this stage to have her investigated.'

Elena found that Gregor was looking not at Córdoba but herself, with a surprised, almost incredulous expression.

'But *you* know. Surely?'

215

'No. I had never heard of her until you mentioned her name to me, in hospital.'

'But your mother — she knows. She named her to me at Valdoro.'

'Then Carlos must have told her. She didn't tell me.'

'What! Then you don't — '

'Gregor,' the Colonel interposed smoothly, 'this isn't getting us very far. If de Zurga is going to use her name for scandal I really must know if he has any grounds. Is she a security risk?'

'Security risk! *Hombre*! That's laughable!'

But Córdoba's face was serious, though he showed no emotion.

'Then — forgive me, my friend, I must ask this. I know you would not go for the obvious purpose, but is she — ? You must have known it was foolish to visit her if, as de Zurga says, she is a prostitute.'

'A *prostitute*! *Dios*, man, are you mad?'

He turned his head quickly and caught the look of relief which lightened Elena's face. His straight brows drew together, his eyes narrowed, his lower lip was out-thrust as always when he spoke with emotion.

'So that's what he told you! And you believed it. *Jesús*, what a high opinion you've got of me!'

'No, I didn't believe it. I didn't know what to think.'

'But you didn't trust me, did you? So that's why your wedding announcement wasn't cancelled. You thought you might as well settle for the devil you knew, even a decadent womanizer, since he has two great advantages — he's stinking rich, and he's an hidalgo, so you don't have to step out of your class.'

'Gregor, for God's sake!' Córdoba broke in urgently. 'Can't you wait for an explanation? Señorita Moural, tell him — are you going to marry de Zurga?'

'No. I broke off the engagement this morning.'

'Congratulations!' Gregor blazed. 'Why? Did he go a bit too far with you before the ceremony? I hope we keep him in the

Army till he rots! I suppose that left you free to come and tell Cordóba here what was stewing in his corrupt little mind!'

'Gregor — listen!'

The Colonel leaned over the desk to him, his expression, his whole attitude demanding attention.

'Señorita Moural only agreed to marry de Zurga to stop him from launching his scandals about you. Can't you get that into your thick head?'

Gregor's face paled as Elena watched. He sat there in silence, staring at the Colonel, his jaw and mouth tightening, his brows contracting. When he turned to her his cold hard gaze thrust like a knife. His voice was low and thick.

'*So you did that*? And am I supposed to thank you? What must I say? That I am honoured by your high opinion of me? You didn't know what to believe, but it was a sporting chance I'd visited a high-class brothel! Did your mother tell you to shield Raquel Mendoza, knowing she didn't need it any more than I did?

'I'm sorry to disappoint you, but you'd have martyred yourself for nothing! And I'm not grateful for the chance of hiding my reputation, whatever it may be, behind a woman's skirts — least of all, yours! Did I ask you to buy de Zurga off — and at *that* price? *Sangre de Cristo! You make me feel like a pimp!*'

Elena hardly knew how she got out of the room.

Couldn't Gregor see that he had just smashed her love, her hopes, her life, and thrown the pieces in her face? After the unchecked bitter flow of his words no one spoke, it seemed for an immeasurable space of time, She sat gazing at him in horror, and behind the desk the Colonel was fixed, petrified with amazement. Gregor's last phrase with all its implications hung like a Gorgon's head between them.

She had endured so much, she had put herself on the rack to help him — and this was his thanks. He thought no more of her than of any passer-by in the street. Indeed, less, 'least of all' — he considered her as decadent as Carlos.

For the moment she was numbed with shock. She knew she

217

had to get out before feeling returned, before her already-tightening throat had time to swell and choke her, before her eyes pricking with tears had a chance to overflow and blind her, before her outward composure collapsed in ruin with her grief.

A cold hard little voice which was her own said, 'Good morning, Colonel. I have no more to tell you.'

Her automaton body took her outside, through the corridors and down the stairs, through the hall to the street, into a taxi and somehow, still as if in a frozen shell, as far as the Avenida de Mayo.

CHAPTER FIFTEEN

It would be a long time before Elena would cease to be haunted by the thought of Gregor sitting in the darkness bleeding to the point of death. Vicente had not said much, but the memory was vivid in his mind, and in a few phrases the picture had been made hideously plain. And for what? Because he had decided her mother was 'up to something', that if it was so important to keep them apart then he must see her as soon as possible. And for what? So that he could have her promise that she would not marry Carlos, and to tell her that his visits to Doña Raquel had not been intended to hurt her.

It was utterly quixotic, fantastic, inexplicable. Even if he cared for her most deeply he could have done no more. But he didn't care, or how could he have brushed her off so angrily when she had been trying to help him? For days in the Avenida de Mayo she had waited in vain, hoping he would ring. One word of friendship would have been enough and she would have gone to him. She didn't want an apology.

But what could she expect? She had repaid him, so he believed, by breaking her word and engaging herself to Carlos, and by thinking the worst of him over Doña Raquel. Her aunt's comment, intended to excuse him, had bitten deep into her conscience. 'Nothing wounds a man so much as finding a woman doesn't trust him. Whether she is justified or not is immaterial'. In her heart of hearts she knew she had not trusted him completely, unquestioningly. So whatever his reasons had been, he had finished with her now.

When, after the two days of waiting Vicente had come to the Avenida de Mayo, it had seemed too ironic for words. He actually knew Doña Raquel. She was the daughter of the famous architect, José Santilla, and occupied the flat he had been granted in the apartment block he had designed. He preferred to live out of town. He had recently suffered a heart attack, Señora Mendoza had been called away . . . it was quite ridiculously plausible.

Yes, he knew the General had visited her — 'on a matter of business, I believe' — but he would not be drawn on Señora Mendoza and would volunteer no more information. So that was that.

And then, to Elena's surprise, she received a letter from Señora Mendoza herself, asking her to call: she had some information to give Elena.

Raquel Mendoza wiped her hands on a turpentine rag and said to her visitor, 'I'd better not shake hands. I'd make you smell. Do sit down.'

She took off her washed-out blue cotton smock, dropped it on her painting stool and left the studio end of the large room.

Elena Moural was now sitting on the couch, looking about her in a very well-bred way, trying not to show any surprise at the Santilla-Mendoza living-room. No doubt it struck her as odd to have a room furnished at one end as a very modern drawing-room and at the other as an artist's studio.

'I was beginning to think you might not come. I was wondering whether I ought to have asked Vicente to bring you.'

'Of course, you know Señor Vargas.'

The polite formal response. And all the time she must be wondering about the letter, and what the information was that she was to be given.

'You can call him Vicente here. I know all about it — how he used to be in love with you, and had to give you up.'

Elena was not used to such frank speaking, but she took it well. Without dissembling she answered, 'Yes. I felt the same about him. But we've both got over it now. Vicente told me that your father is Señor Santilla the architect, but he didn't say that you are an artist.'

'He probably forgot, he's so used to it. Are you interested

in painting? If so, look around. This is all my stuff. Excuse me, there's something I want to show you.'

Elena watched Raquel Mendoza as she hurried out of the room. What a strange young woman she was! Very emancipated and independent, one would think, but attractive; full of contrasts. Men would probably find her fascinating, her femininity would attract them, and her nonchalance intrigue them. Her looks were appealing; she wore her hair cut short in a style like a boy's — it might not be a style, just a matter of convenience, but it added to her gamine look. Her face was too broad for beauty, but her eyes were lovely, slightly slanting, dark and almond-shaped, and she had a full, wide but sensitive mouth.

She was thoroughly unconventional, or how else could she write a letter to a complete stranger, saying she had information which they ought to know, and when they turned up for the proposed interview, talk away and tell them nothing?

Elena had been invited to look at the canvases. There were plenty in the studio end of the room, stacked against the walls, some finished, some not. They were everywhere except in an area round the large window under which a drawing board was fixed.

The easel where Raquel Mendoza had been working stood nearby, next to a table covered with paints and brushes and artist's paraphernalia. On the easel was a half-finished still life; it had style and promised to be very good. Against the end wall were abstracts, a couple of landscapes, and a lively portrait of a young girl.

From other canvases other faces looked at her, and in the drawing-room end of the apartment hung two more portraits, of a man and a woman. Elena guessed that the subjects were Raquel Mendoza's parents.

At the sound of footsteps she turned to see Doña Raquel coming into the room carrying quite a small canvas, about half a metre in length, the back facing outwards.

'This is what I wanted to show you, and why I asked you here.' Doña Raquel sounded a trifle breathless. 'You'd better

221

sit down.'

Surprised, Elena obeyed. She was thinking she couldn't begin to understand this strange young woman, really Vicente should have warned her if he knew they would be meeting.

Doña Raquel stood in front of her, and turning the canvas held it before her eyes.

Elena stared, and went on staring, as the shock struck her and sent her senses spinning in a whirlpool of incredulity, beyond reasoning or thought. And as she stared a face looked back at her across the years, a handsome face, debonair and unconcerned. Her brother Luis.

'Luis! Luis – '

Was that her voice? It must have been, for Doña Raquel nodded.

'You knew my brother?'

As she tried to fight her feeling of stupefaction Doña Raquel replied. 'He was my husband.'

Elena rode the second shock, clutching the portrait in both hands, looking from it to Doña Raquel. Her voice when it came was almost a whisper.

'Why did we never know?'

Doña Raquel gave her a crooked smile. 'Thank you – for not saying "I don't believe you".'

'Why should you lie? But I wish I understood – Luis never told us. I didn't even know your name.'

'I want to explain. There's a lot to tell you. Do you smoke?' Elena shook her head. 'Well, I need one.'

Doña Raquel took a cigarette from a box on a nearby table, lit it, and paused for a few moments longer before starting her story.

'We met quite by accident, when Luis was in his last year at the university. At first I had no thought of it becoming a serious friendship. I knew who he was, and that I wasn't in his class. Don't think I felt inferior, I didn't, but my family and their friends are all professional people or artists or intellectuals, and titled landowners don't usually mix with progressives if they can help it. I was surprised when he kept making

222

opportunities to see me, and I found that, rather against my will, I was growing fond of him. So I told him that I couldn't see him any more.'

'But why, if you were beginning to like him?'

'*Because* of that. I didn't want to be dominated by a man — any man — who might want me to lead a conventional social life and push my painting into the few odd minutes that were left. But also because I had the sense to see that it would only lead to trouble.'

She made a sweeping gesture. 'I said to myself, "Cut loose before you get hurt. He'll soon find somebody else. Stick to your painting." He was so charming, I knew he could have any girl he wanted, so he'd far better pick one his family could approve.'

'But why shouldn't we approve of you?'

'Why? *You* ask *why*?'

She stubbed out her cigarette, then turned to Elena with a savage abruptness. 'Being out of your class was enough, but in addition — well, look at me!'

'Why? What's wrong with you?'

Elena was bewildered by the sudden outburst for which she could see no reason.

'Look at me, and you can see that my great-great-grandmother was a pure-blood Indian.'

Elena drew in her breath, and stared. 'It never occurred to me!' she cried, and added angrily: 'And I don't see that it matters!'

'That's funny, I thought you would care, but you don't, any more than Luis did. He really didn't mind, but that wasn't enough. So we didn't see each other for nearly a year. Then he came to me and told me he had tried, but he couldn't be happy without me.

'Soon we were seeing a lot of each other — my family have modern ideas, I had no duena, I was trusted to behave sensibly. So we were able to get to know each other well. And then we were desperately in love, we knew there couldn't be anyone else for either of us. But I wouldn't marry him, and much as we loved each other he wouldn't ask me for anything else.'

'But you *did* marry him — why not then?'

'Because of your parents, of course! I heard how your mother had treated Vicente, and if I had been in any doubt, one incident clinched it.'

'What was that?'

'I heard her say in public — not of a group of field-labourers, but of a number of our finest artists — "What a collection of mixed bloods! I should think one in three is a half-breed! How can you expect me to stay?" — That from a completely idle, uncreative woman! I was so disgusted I walked straight past them and cut Luis as if I didn't know him.'

'And what happened?'

'He ran me to earth after she had gone. We had a scene, our only real quarrel. He said his father would understand, but I knew that wasn't enough. I told him he was never to mention my name to his family. I don't care that I'm "mixed", it means nothing to me, and Luis didn't mind, I'm sure of that, but I wasn't prepared to be humiliated by his family and friends because of it, and I couldn't stand the thought of the effect such treatment would have on him if he married me. But we couldn't stop meeting.

'Then your father died and the Civil War started. Luis, I could tell, was getting desperate. We weren't exactly in opposite camps, my family have always been pretty neutral over politics, but Luis felt he must defend Valdoro and the old régime, and yet he wanted me. And I felt I couldn't go on refusing him. He was of age, he was the Conde, his mother no longer had any right to dictate to him. I agreed to marry him under certain conditions.'

Elena was hanging on every word, trying to imagine what it had been like for Doña Raquel.

'What were the conditions?'

'First of all, that the marriage was to be kept secret, for the time at least. That meant that only my parents, and one or two people like Vicente, whom we needed and could trust, were told. And Luis was never to ask me to live under the same roof as his mother. He died before I let him tell his family. When I heard about his death I was glad you didn't know.'

Elena turned to her in compassion. 'You never saw him afterwards — you've not even seen his grave.'

'I'm glad. I'm not one for funerals. Why should I want to see a wounded body? I can remember him like this.'

Her hands enclosed the portrait in a tender gesture that was like an embrace.

'Did Vicente tell you?'

'Yes. The whole business of Luis's death affected him terribly. I don't think he will ever quite get over it. I haven't helped him by making him keep silent all these years. But that was how I wanted it, until now. And even now, I'm not sure.'

It was not until then that Elena realized the one fact which should have registered with her from the first moment of revelation. As it swept over her, she turned swiftly to Doña Raquel, and spoke without jealousy or rancour, her voice holding no emotion other than surprised acceptance.

'But it's right! All these years since Luis's death, we have been at Valdoro. But it's not ours. Valdoro belongs to you!'

Doña Raquel lit another cigarette, and there was a long pause before she spoke.

'You wouldn't contest that, then?'

Elena looked at her in amazement. 'Of course not! As Luis's widow you inherit.'

'How do you know I'm his widow? You've only my word.'

'I imagine you must have some proof.'

'Yes, I have. It's all with Señor Castellán. That's why I wanted to see you today. I thought Luis would want me to break the truth to you in private, rather than for you to be faced with it in a lawyer's office. I couldn't offer the same consideration to your mother, for the simple reason that I can imagine what her reaction will be.'

Elena said nothing.

And so can you. First she'll say I'm lying. Then, when she's shown the proof, she'll say I trapped Luis into marriage. She'll insult my ancestry, question my morals — she won't spare me a thing.'

Elena covered Raquel's hand with her own. 'I like you, and I believe you. You *must* have Valdoro.'

'Valdoro? Oh, well, we shall see what the will says. The fact that there was a will was another secret I made Vicente keep. When he found Luis — dead — he guessed there might be a letter for me. Valdoro was much nearer than where I was living, and he felt you ought to be told, but he had promised Luis and me not to reveal our marriage. So he made himself search Luis's body. There was a letter, with Luis's wedding ring and a copy of his will. Vicente took them, and as soon as he could he brought them to me.

'I already had a copy of the will, but Vicente didn't know that, and to be quite honest he didn't trust your mother not to destroy all the papers if they fell into her hands. Perhaps he was unjust, but he'd had experience of her and he says she's a ruthless woman, which I can well believe.'

Elena was finding it quite hard to pull herself together. She had had a shock this morning, but that was no excuse for near-hysterical giggling. It might be as well to change the subject to something unemotional.

'Why do you call yourself Mendoza?' she asked.

'It's my mother's name. I started using it when I first took up art professionally. My father's name was established, and I had no wish to trade on it. After I married Luis I couldn't call myself Moural, it's too well known not to provoke questions. The secret would have been out in no time.'

'May I call you Raquel?'

'Of course.'

'Then, Raquel, I must be honest with you. My mother and I will owe you a great deal of money, and I think you will have a hard legal fight to get it. You see, much as I would like to give you my share, I have no access to any money without my mother's permission, and she will not be likely to pay you

226

anything herself until she is forced to do so.'

Raquel nodded. 'I realize that.'

'It's going to be such a complicated situation. My mother sold the town house after Luis's death, she has sold the entire stud, all our bloodstock, there are only the working horses in the *tropillas* left. We have been using your land — and there's the money paid on the sequestration, she has it all. I don't see how you can be compensated without a long legal battle.'

Raquel looked at her curiously. 'Why do you think I've put the will in the lawyer's hands after so long?'

'To get your legal rights, why else?'

'It's not quite that. I have all the money I want, and I don't give a damn for Valdoro — why should I? Vicente started it, he worried me to come forward. He said your mother was going to sell the *estancia*, that it was wrong, that I'd let things slide too long and I should do what Luis wanted, that Valdoro should stay with a Moural.

'I'm not a Moural, but I could see his argument. I should have respected Luis's wishes — but we didn't have a child . . . we had so little married life, and it just didn't happen . . . but while Luis was fighting he might have had one and never known . . . he provided for that possibility, among other things . . . .'

She paused for moment, and when she spoke again her voice became brisk once more.

'As it was, it didn't matter to me. I thought it best for you both to keep Valdoro. Then Vicente kept telling me that you cared about the place, that you didn't want it sold, that your mother was treating you badly, that Luis wouldn't have allowed it, and so on. Then he said that legal rights should be established and brought in General Marint to back him up.'

'So that was why he came here!'

'You knew? The General said he was concerned that the right will should be proved, because he might have made an error in the sequestration.'

'What sort of an error? How?'

'If the land were to be divided under the will the State

227

would not be entitled to confiscate as much as if it were a single holding, you know that.'

'Divided? But it won't be divided – it's yours. That will make no difference.'

'But the General wants to know that his Ministry has acted correctly. And although he said very little about you, except how well you had run the *estancia*, I think he agreed with Vicente that you might be better off under Luis's will than you are at present. After all, even a little ready money would be useful. When Vicente was out of town the General came several times to see me, persuading me to have the will proved.'

'So you're doing it for me?'

'No, nothing so noble! I'm doing it to prevent your mother selling Valdoro, since the Mourales seem to think it matters. The General said you would rather it went to your brother's widow than to any other stranger. I told him I wasn't so sure – that you didn't know me and wouldn't want to. Although he didn't say much he spoke so well of you, he convinced me that you weren't like your mother. In fact, I don't think a possible Ministerial error was his only concern.'

'No,' Elena answered gravely. 'He came because he wanted to help me. But he knew my mother would say he was urging you to take Valdoro away from us. Now I understand what he meant. If only I'd known . . . He said, "I went, but not to hurt you . . . " '

Raquel gazed at her. There were tears in Elena's eyes.

'I'm sorry. Perhaps it won't be as bad as you think.'

This will cause a fine sensation, thought Doña Ana. There is enough in this affair to rattle the coffee cups of Varena society for weeks. To think that Luis had contracted a clandestine marriage, had died keeping his secret, and that the marriage and the will he had made had only now come to light.

Elena had been convinced of the truth of Raquel's story from the first, and now Señor Castellán, satisfied by the proofs, was taking steps to enforce Luis's will. It would take a long time to get everything straightened out, because one thing was certain; he would get no co-operation from Luisa.

Soon the family would be split from top to bottom — one side for Luisa, and one for Elena and Raquel. Besides that litigation, Elena was petitioning for the release of the money left to her by her father. She would get it of course, as soon as her case was considered. But in the meantime, what would she do?

Doña Ana had the odd feeling that she must have spoken her thoughts aloud, for as if in answer she heard Elena saying 'I must get to Valdoro as soon as possible.'

'*Querida*, you're not serious! You can't mean to go back by yourself!'

'It's the only sensible thing to do.'

'Sensible! It's madness! In any case, the will isn't proved yet ... your mother will contest it ... you'll need to be in Varena.'

'Of course Mother will contest it. And who knows how long it will take to get a legal ruling? I can't hang around in Varena.'

Doña Ana converted her concern for Elena into annoyance with her sister-in-law.

'Luisa is quite impossible! This should have been done when Luis died, then there would have been some chance of enforcing it. Luisa is very lucky to have been left the town house and the plantations -- and a tidy sum.'

'Luis saw it all very clearly. He knew that Mother and Raquel would never agree, and he wanted to ensure that Mother had some capital and income besides her own money. And I think he must have guessed that Mother and I might fall out sooner or later. He saw the beginnings of it when I first refused Carlos, and when -- when I was in love with Vicente.'

'Yes. He had to make provision for you independently. All the same, he must have expected that you would marry.'

'You mean he wouldn't have expected me to live alone at Valdoro? That's nothing to do with it. He knew Raquel didn't want the house. She had told him she wouldn't set foot in it

229

while Mother was there, and even if Mother left she had no intention of living in it — '

'Not even if they'd had a child?'

'Not even then. Luis was going to build another house on the far side of the pampa. If they'd had a child, Valdoro house would have gone to it on my death. As it is, it's mine outright.'

'With — apart from the plantations — a half share of the *estancia* land. Is Raquel contented with her half, and the money — if she can get it?'

'Perfectly contented. They discussed it all between them before he put anything in writing. He wanted the house and some of the *estancia* to remain in Moural hands whatever happened. I never knew when he was alive that he cared about Valdoro so much.'

'That must be a bitter pill for Luisa to swallow. She always wanted him to take after her side of the family, and now he's turned out a true Moural after all.'

'So you see, I must get back to Valdoro.'

'No, I don't see! You can't possibly live in that great house by yourself.'

'I shan't be alone, there are still the servants.'

'The servants! They are more of a liability than an asset! There's absolutely no company for you, no one for twenty miles. You'll be like a hermit. You can't live in that solitary fashion.'

'I shall have plenty to do.'

'That's not the point!'

'The point is, Valdoro — the heart of Valdoro — is mine, and I am going to look after it. Raquel says I can run her land together with mine, so in practice I shall have the whole *estancia* — except the plantations, which never interested me very much in any case — to manage. Quite a lot of the sequestered land will come back to us, and I shall be able to concentrate on cattle and horse-breeding. We have plenty of cattle. For horses, I'll have to build up a new stud when I lay hands on some money.

'At present I'll have to learn to live on credit! But if I don't

230

go back soon everything will fall apart. No one will know where the orders ought to come from. Just now Mother is in Varena, concerned with Cristina's wedding. But as soon as that is over she'll want to fight Raquel and me, and her first action will be to try to get her hands on Valdoro. But, as you've said before, possession is nine points of the law, and if I'm there with a lawyer's letter to back me up, I shall stay. And anyone doing business over Valdoro stock will do it with me.'

As Doña Ana sat digesting this there was a knock on the drawing-room door and Josefina came in holding a square white envelope which she gave to her mistress.

Doña Ana, having opened it, looked in surprise at the card it held.

'I think you'll be here for a few days longer, *querida*.'

'Why, Aunt?'

She passed over the card to Elena. 'I hope you don't propose to refuse an invitation from the President! You see, it's for both of us — an informal reception.'

'. . . in honour of those people, both Riquezans and our foreign friends, who have given notable service to our country; and later at the Ball . . .' Elena read it aloud. And caught her breath.

CHAPTER SIXTEEN

Doña Ana and Elena had been at the reception a bare ten minutes when they were pounced upon by the two young United States doctors, Alvin Jarrett and Tom Callaway.

The *Norte-Americanos* were charming and delightful, Elena thought. They were just a little naïve, perhaps; but then no doubt so would she be about their way of life if she were suddenly sent to New York. They were still eager for information, plying Doña Ana and herself with questions; social customs, music, national costumes, food, everything was coming under review.

It was necessary to talk loudly amid the general hubbub; animated conversations were in progress all around, and the chinking of glasses was overlaid by the strains of music throbbing from the next room. If one did not stand quite close to one's companions one ran the risk of being temporarily swept away by the movement of other people eddying around.

Jarrett and Callaway had established themselves one on either side of her; she was simultaneously soothed by the respectful tone of their voices and stimulated by the undisguised admiration in their eyes. But one thing was obsessing her.

Gregor Marint was here. He could not be far away. Had she subconsciously registered the timbre of his voice among all the other voices, or heard someone speak his name?

Whatever the reason, there was a little pulse of excitement. of anticipation beating within her, she could feel it fluttering like a tiny moth at the base of her throat. Could she dare to look for him? If he ignored her or gave her cutting courtesy how could she bear it? How long before she was brave enough to look?

Her sentences were drifting away, the thread of thought quite lost, but it didn't matter. In a moment she would know for certain. She would know whether he would come forward or merely bow and turn away. She would know whether there was any hope at all.

She lifted her head and looked.

He was standing apart, his eyes upon her. He did not move, nor did his expression change, but his eyes held hers with an intense gaze which made her want to walk across to him — how many paces? — ten — fifteen — and offer him her hand so that he would have to take it in his.

Why couldn't she do it? No, of course she couldn't. It would be too familiar — 'immodest' her mother would have said. It would make her most conspicuous.

If only Aunt Ana would turn round and see him, she could and would invite him over. Why couldn't the wretched *Yanquis* leave her? If she were alone he might come to her instead of standing there, his face saying nothing, just his eyes burning. Was he too proud to make a move until he knew . . . ? She was proud, but not too proud. There must be a way . . .

Then the generations of *dueña*-guarded girls, the close cherished Moural women who had lived before her gave her their weapons, the inheritance of her breeding urged her to her first deliberate act of coquetry with him. She dipped her chin a little and began to smile.

With a flick of the wrist her fan flared open, then began to move rhythmically, delicately, enticingly, reinforcing the invitation in her eyes. Any man would have guessed — to a Riquezan the language of the fan was as certain as speech. For the space of several seconds Gregor watched.

Then he turned and stubbed out his cigarillo. She caught her breath. He was turning away. No — he began to move towards her.

He came straight across with that easy, loose stride that was so deceptively quick. A waiter with a tray of full glasses misjudged it and had to pull up short; Gregor, without checking, removed a glass from the tray as he passed and came

233

on, to halt in front of her. She let her fan drop to hang from her wrist. Without a word he bowed and offered her the glass.

The pale wine was settling round the rim; his hand was brown and square, rock-steady. Did he know what his gesture implied in her tradition? She raised her eyes to his. He must know. Willing her hand not to tremble she took the glass. It was cold in her hand, she wanted to feel the warm touch of his fingers but they slid away without contact. Neither of them spoke. He stood close to her and his eyes did not leave her face as slowly she raised the wine-glass to her lips.

'Am I forgiven?' he asked quietly.

Her glance flashed up to meet his, his brown face was bent to hers. 'Yes,' she whispered.

His nearness made her feel weak, all resistance had melted out of her, if he had taken her hand she would have let him lead her anywhere.

'Why, General Marint, how nice to see you!' Doña Ana raised her voice. 'Shall we go into the next room? Dancing has started — I'm sure some of you would like to join in before the Ball begins — then there will be such a crush.'

What was in Gregor Marint's mind? Doña Ana wondered as he had made no attempt to dance with Elena.

Surely he wasn't playing with her? He was too honourable a man for that. Did he only want her friendship? To Elena that might be worse than indifference. Was that why she was so insistent on returning to Valdoro? Did she want to bury herself there and try to forget him? Poor child, she was breaking her heart, and there was nothing one could do if Marint didn't care. Only he could help, and he seemed to be holding aloof with an obstinacy as harsh as it was inexplicable.

The Ball was now in full swing, and although Elena was never without a partner it would not be surprising if she suggested leaving. They were both being treated with a marked frostiness by hidalgo society. It didn't bother *her*. She herself had weathered more than one freeze in her lifetime, and emerged the victor to enjoy the warmth again, but Elena might be more sensitive.

234

There had been a very awkward moment when Elena had come face to face with Luisa, Cristina and her *novio*, Jorge Morillo. Elena had smiled, but Luisa, her own mother, had stared at her as if she did not know her and then pointedly turned away. It could not have been a more obvious cut.

The smile had faded from Elena's face, but she had pulled herself together and behaved with admirable dignity and composure.

News of the family feud would be all over Varena tomorrow. It was already strongly rumoured, and confirmation would fly from lip to lip. Elena must be feeling very hurt; one could only hope she would not also feel humiliated by being the subject of gossip. There was no reason why she should. She was quite right to support Raquel. Still, it was not going to be easy, and there were signs of partisanship among people who had observed the encounter.

Society being what it was, it would be solidly for Luisa. Elena would be considered a traitor to her mother and a rebel against parental control since everyone knew Luisa had wanted her to marry Carlos.

Gregor Marint had been at the reception from the beginning. There were people he had to talk to, but once that was done, provided he mixed and made himself pleasant he could consider his duty discharged. That left him plenty of scope; not like Ramón, who, looking and behaving like the perfect socialite, was really being the perfect Chief of Police. With so many visiting foreigners he was one hundred per cent on duty. But a general could do much as he pleased.

So Gregor Marint strolled about the reception rooms, outwardly urbane and relaxed, inwardly crackling with impatience. Elena must come. He had seen the list, and her name was on it. And it was the right occasion for an accidental meeting.

It must look accidental now. He could not commit himself any further until he knew her attitude, her feelings towards him. He wanted her — *Dios*, how he wanted her! Absence had

235

not lessened the desire that gnawed at him. But it was not merely a physical craving. It was much more than that, which made it unique to him, and of a totally unexpected importance.

He had no need to analyse his feelings. He knew all about them. He was sure she was the one woman who could complement him: with her he could achieve so much more. Their aims were basically the same, hers for Valdoro, his for the whole country; and that was only part of the story. Why should the issue be in doubt?

He could rouse her physically, make her love him, he knew that. But that wasn't enough. You couldn't live with a person, love together, work together, without mutual trust. If she didn't trust him, what then? He had only to see her for his blood to cry out his desire. He had tried to remember the lessons of his early manhood, and let disillusion convince him that the body's satisfaction was all one could hope for. But it wasn't so, not with her. It wouldn't be enough for him, nor would it be for her, and to take her on the assumption that their relationship was only physical would doom it from the start.

Yet there were such differences between them. Of class, of outlook, of way of life. It was as if they were on opposite sides of a deep canyon, and trust was the only bridge between them. Was it there? And was it strong enough? Somehow he must find out. Some time – tonight – he couldn't wait any longer.

Acknowledging greeting after greeting with a smile and a nod he had moved up and down, his brain whirling around the thought of Elena. Then he had stopped, lit a cigarillo and begun to look into the farther corners of the room where so many people going to and fro in the intervening space had baulked his first apparently casual glances. And there she was.

She was talking to Doña Ana and two young men. *Yanquis*, he guessed. So he would wait for her to look up and catch his eye. He knew he would not have to wait long. Then she saw him, reacted with only half-concealed confusion; seemed at a loss.

Still he waited, and before long her signal came. The warm glow of triumph spread through him. She had never deliberately used the lure of her femininity to him before, and how delectable it was! She looked irresistible.

He delayed, giving himself the delight of watching her. Then he moved forward to join her.

That the waiter should be there was quite fortuitous; on an impulse he had taken advantage of it to respond to her invitation with a gesture of hidalgo courtship, hoping she would give him the credit for knowing it. In silently handing her the wine after her invitation to join her he had said, 'I am paying court to you.' In tasting it she had answered, 'I accept your admiration.' There were times when these old customs were a good game to play.

And then he apologized, and by that she would know not only that he regretted his angry words but that he knew her own actions had been intended to help him. The apology had pleased her, — he could tell and yet she had immediately turned to the *Yanquis* and given them all her attention.

Was she using them as a smoke-screen to hide her feelings from him? If so, she would find he was not to be teased with such childish tricks. Was she simply keeping him at a distance? If she did not wish to be seen dancing with him at a public function, her affection for him must be infinitesimal, her trust non-existent.

Soon he was raging with anger. Concealing it with bland looks and manner he allowed himself to be engaged in conversation, he danced, he went to and fro — but always he was observing. There might be some other reason; he must give her one more chance to make amends. Happiness was not lightly to be thrown away, his temper had played him false with her before.

So he waited as patiently as he could until the first interval of the Ball; made sure he was not obliged to escort anyone, and then went alone — passing near where she was sitting — ostensibly in search of refreshments.

Doña Ana heaved a sigh of relief. At last it was the interval. She had been dancing with Mr. Russell Comber, Head of the United States Mission of Relief; Elena with Tom Callaway, and Mrs. Comber with Alvin Jarrett, so it was natural for the six of them to group together, Mr. Comber seeing the ladies seated while the two young men went to get them cool drinks.

What a chatterbox Mrs. Comber was! Elena was trying to show polite attention, but anyone who knew her could guess how her interest was flagging. Then Mrs. Comber mentioned Gregor's name.

'. . . and General Marint has been telling me about some of your interesting customs. He was saying that the costume the band is wearing is a kind of fancy version of a *vaquero's* clothes – the gay shirt and neckerchief, and the baggy trousers like – what did he call them?'

'*Bombachas.*'

'Yes, that's the word. And he said that most people had special clothes they wore at *fiestas* – do your family have them?'

She was appealing to Elena.

'We used to.'

'Like those?' Mrs. Comber was burning with curiosity.

'No, of course not!'

If Elena's mind had not been wandering she would not have answered quite like that. There had been a touch of hauteur in her voice, and it had not passed unnoticed. But Tom Callaway had returned and tried to be tactful.

'Señorita Moural wouldn't wear a folk-costume, Mrs. Comber.'

Now Elena realized she might have given offence, and was trying to soften the impression. 'My family wear the Spanish style – because we like it – flounced dresses for the girls and tight suits ornamented with silver for the men.'

'Oh, I hadn't realized there were different ones – ' Mrs. Comber was floundering, and Elena was still trying to help her out.

'There are dozens. This is just one. You see, the *vaquero* is

238

quite a special type in our country. They are splendid horsemen, very independent and brave – and what you would call 'tough'. This fancy costume is a way of showing we admire them. You may have noticed the musicians are even wearing the *boleadora* round their waists.'

'That's the bolas? Isn't it used to bring down cattle instead of a lariat?' Tom Callaway asked.

Now Elena was making amends for her absent-mindedness, and being chatty and informative.

'Yes, but it's not used for that much now. It's an old Indian hunting weapon. Most modern cattle-owners disapprove of it. I won't let my *vaqueros* – ' She paused – did she think that sounded conceited? – but she had gone too far, Mrs. Comber was looking at her questioningly. 'I was only going to say that I won't let my *vaqueros* use it except in an emergency. When cattle are brought down with it they sometimes break a leg and have to be shot.'

'I see.' Now Mrs. Comber was thoughtful, weighing her up. 'Do you have many *vaqueros*?'

'Not so many now,' Elena hedged. 'Some were transferred to the State Farm when part of the *estancia* was sequestered.'

'Oh, some of your land was taken? By General Marint?'

'By his Ministry.'

'Was that what he meant when he asked if he was forgiven?'

Dios! People with such sharp ears ought to learn to curb their curiosity! Taken off guard, Elena stammered, 'No – yes – something like that – '

Gregor Marint was only a few paces away, but he was weaving through the crush towards the buffet tables. Doña Ana watched Elena follow the direction of her glance, see him, and turn a shade paler. Why didn't he come over?

Now, to add to Elena's trials, Don Pablo was joining them. He eased himself on to the too-small chair and words began to rumble from him.

'Ana, my dear, when this is over you must let me escort you and Elena home.'

'Thank you, Pablo, but there's no need. We won't deprive

239

Luisa of your company.'

Pablo's look was reproachful, she had the feeling his growls were the first warnings of a volcanic eruption.

'Elena is a single girl, and after so much attention from these *Yanquis* a man of your family should be seen to take you home.'

It was quite laughable. Like all the de Zurgas, Pablo was living in the past, allowing himself and his menfolk unlimited licence, but keeping his women with the utmost strictness.

'I have been dancing with different partners,' Elena said pointedly. 'Nothing can be made of that.'

He looked at her sharply.

'No, not of *that*. But my fear is that those partners may well have the wrong impression of you. *Yanquis* need no encouragement — and they saw your earlier behaviour. I hope none of our people did — I was shocked.'

Thank heaven Pablo was speaking in Spanish. Elena's lips set firmly.

'And precisely what about my behaviour was so shocking?'

'You were actually flirting! It would be quite bad enough to invite someone of your own class in public to come and speak to you — but someone like Marint! A fellow of no class — and a doubtful reputation! I am thankful he realized I was prepared to guard the proprieties, and has kept away! If anyone who matters saw you — '

Elena was boiling with anger. 'I don't care who saw me! *He* saw me, which was what I intended. And I'll thank you to leave me to guard my own morals!'

He stared at her, outraged. 'You cannot afford this behaviour! In your position you should be very circumspect — '

'My position! What is *my position*?'

'I shouldn't need to tell you! You are single, without close male relatives, you have been disowned by your mother, you have no money, no promised *novio* — if you hope to marry you had better not rouse any more suspicions.'

'How dare you!' Elena rose to her feet. 'Do you think I care what you, or anyone like you, suspects of me? Are you afraid I shall be gossiped over? From now on I do what *I* choose with my life!'

And now she was scanning the buffet tables. On a number of faces interest and curiosity deepened, while Pablo looked on in increasing horror as Elena identified Gregor Marint's back and walked firmly across, to stand quite deliberately as close to him as she could find a place.

CHAPTER SEVENTEEN

Doña Ana caught her breath and watched. That was the first rattle of artillery; at any moment the big guns would open up. Pablo was standing as if transfixed; when he had assimilated his feeling of outrage he would move. It looked as if there was going to be a battle — military metaphors kept leaping to her mind — it would be Pablo against Gregor Marint, with Elena caught in the cross-fire — though Pablo, of course, was representing all the forces of family and class and traditional upbringing. And a fine representative he was!

But Marint was still an unknown quantity. What did he want of Elena, if anything? He had been so aloof. She did not believe in meddling, but if Elena needed her help . . . Pablo wiped his hand across his face and took a determined pace forward.

He was actually going to follow Elena, she could see that was his intention. But Elena must be given her chance to speak to Marint. Surprised at her own turn of speed she had caught Pablo's arm before he had taken three steps.

'Are you getting some refreshments, Pablo? I'll come with you.'

He could not prevent his brows from giving a twitch of annoyance. 'Don't bother, Ana, I'll bring you some.'

'It's no bother. I'll show you what I want and you shall get it for me.'

They went to the buffet table. It was crowded. Whatever happened they would have a ready-made audience, she thought grimly. He tried to edge her towards Elena, but she indicated that clean plates were farther down, and watched him reluctantly go to fetch her one.

Then, turning, she saw that Gregor Marint had by-passed

242

the people between himself and Elena and was offering her a dish of savouries. She heaved a sigh of relief. Now they must have a chance to talk.

There was a hubbub of chatter all around, a clinking of glasses and clatter of plates, but through it all she could distinguish their two voices. Emotional concern seemed to have turned her into a human radio set tuned on to their wave-length.

Gregor Marint wasn't bothering to talk quietly. Without the slightest compunction she listened, anxious to hear as much as possible. She must try to give them time to come to some understanding.

' . . . having invited me to address myself to you, did you have a change of heart? Are the *Yanquis* for amusement — or protection?'

There was a hard core to the bantering tone of his voice.

Elena looked up at him swiftly. 'For protection. But not against you.' Her words were low, but clear and urgent.

'So? Someone else? Who? Oh, it doesn't matter. Then you'll dance with me?'

Another look, another smile. 'Yes, if you'll ask me.'

'I'm asking you now.'

Oh, confound Pablo de Zurga! He was at her elbow, offering her a plate, his glance lifting over her shoulder to Elena. He must be kept away. Doña Anna heard her own voice trilling out.

'I'll have one of these canapés — and Pablo, would you be so good as to get me a glass of fruit cup? I am so thirsty. Down there at the end of the table — it will be much more refreshing.'

Frustration and resentment struggled with politeness, but politeness won. Off he went again, and she returned her ears to Marint and Elena. Ah, there was Marint's voice.

' . . . is it true that you've quarrelled with your mother?'

'Yes.'

'Why?'

'Because I refused to marry on her direction.'

243

A burst of laughter behind her drowned Marint's reply, and their next exchanges. When she picked them up again Elena was saying, ' . . . getting used to it. And I have Valdoro.'

His retort came, quick and hard-edged. 'Is Valdoro still a substitute for human relationships?'

She answered swiftly, defensively. 'No. But it's all I have.'

'It need not be.'

Ah, that was better. *Dios*! Here was Pablo again, practically thrusting the glass into her hand and moving past her. She could not stop him. But Elena could see him coming.

'Elena!'

Heads turned as Pablo called her name over the noise – he probably had not intended to shout so loud.

Elena spoke hurriedly to Marint. 'Let's go back to the others.'

'Don't you want to talk to me?'

'Elena!'

Pablo's voice cut in; Marint ignored it, and continued. 'Not that one can talk here with any privacy.'

'Elena!'

She gestured him back, and answered Marint. 'Yes, I do – but how can we?'

'We will.'

'*Elena*!'

Gregor appeared to see Pablo for the first time. He spoke quietly but very clearly, in tones of the utmost politeness. 'What is wrong with that elderly gentleman?'

Amused glances flashed over several faces, and a dark flush mounted in Pablo's cheeks.

Elena had to intervene. 'Gregor, this is Don Pablo de Zurga. Haven't you met? Pablo, this is – '

'I know who it is.' Pablo's thick voice dropped the words with measured hidalgo insolence. Gregor was unmoved.

'De Zurga. The name's familiar. I mean, quite apart from being so well known it seems to have some significance for me. Ah, now I have it. We drafted someone of that name into the Army a couple of months ago.'

He began to pile a plate with canapés, selecting them with careful consideration as he talked. Pablo looked too indignant for speech. Around them eating and drinking were being suspended; people were turning to face them like bees about the queen in a hive.

'Normally I wouldn't know, of course. But this fellow distinguished himself.'

'Indeed? How?' Curiosity forced the words from Pablo's lips.

'He tried to buy himself out before he was even officially in. Never known such indecent haste. Was he any relation?'

'He is my eldest son. It was all a mistake.'

Pablo seemed in danger of choking.

'It certainly was. Well, you did the right thing.' Marint gave Pablo's arm a reassuring pat, then returned to the canapés. 'Best thing for everybody. The money's useful to the Army — the lad wasn't. We'd never have made a soldier of him. Not the type at all. Hadn't the guts.'

Pablo stood, purple-faced, speechless.

'Why, hello, General Marint!' A figure was thrusting itself through the onlookers. Mrs. Comber advanced upon the group, eyes and teeth shining. 'I've been looking for you all over!'

The blonde mopstick of a woman had pushed her way through the crowd, and was confronting Gregor Marint.

'Oh — am I interrupting?'

Gregor smiled. 'Nothing of any importance.'

He offered her the plate and she helped herself.

'Thanks! Now, General, won't you and Señorita Moural tell me some more about life on the pampas?'

Everyone relaxed. With the *Norte-Americana* appropriating the General there would be an end to the private *corrida* which had promised to be so entertaining.

Attention was drawn back to the food and drink, and Doña Ana began to view the arrival of Mrs. Comber with only slightly less enthusiasm than she would have accorded to a visitation from the Angel Gabriel. Elena looked relieved and Pablo nonplussed. Mrs. Comber continued to demand Gregor's

245

attention.

'That bolas thing you were telling me about — I've never seen one. Señorita Moural says it isn't used now?'

'Oh, it's still used,' Gregor replied, with a quick smile at Elena. 'Not by good cattlemen, but as Señorita Moural can tell you, it has three purposes — for hunting, for showing off, and for dancing.'

'My, you'll have to explain that!'

'It explains itself. Some use it to catch game — and some to catch women!'

'Tell me more!'

'It is simple. A *vaquero* prides himself on doing everything he wants to do better than most men, whether it's riding, herding, dancing, or courting women. And the *boleadora* is his universal weapon. You say you have never seen one?'

'No, never. Not close to.'

'Then excuse me for a few moments and I will try to get one for you.'

He was walking away in the direction of the orchestra. If she could draw Pablo off before he came back, leaving Elena talking to Mrs. Comber . . . but Pablo was still hovering over Elena, it wouldn't be easy.

'What did the General mean about dancing and courting women, Señorita Moural?'

Elena politely focused her attention on Mrs. Comber.

'I think he was referring to the fact that the *vaqueros* use the *boleadora* in one of their special courting dances.'

'What's special about it?'

Pablo, whom she had hoped to distract, suddenly came bulldozing into the conversation.

'It is of no importance, Mrs. Comber. One does not bother with the peasant dances, it is most unlikely you will see it performed.'

'But I've heard the peasant dances are marvellous!' She glanced vivaciously about her; Doña Ana tried to make herself inconspicuous, but too late — she was pounced upon. 'Have you seen that dance, Señora Carvelo?'

'Of course,' she found herself replying, in spite of Pablo's look of heavy disapproval. 'I was born and bred at Valdoro like Elena — and we always watched the *vaqueros* when they had their celebrations.'

'And have you danced it yourself?'

Again Pablo took over. 'That would be quite impossible, Mrs. Comber. It would not be fitting.'

'Now you have roused my curiosity! Then who does dance it?'

Pablo's mouth drooped and his eyes blinked as if he had been asked something indelicate.

'Only the *vaqueros* and their women, Mrs. Comber. And a *vaquero* who dances it with an unmarried girl and does not propose to her afterwards will find himself in trouble — unless, of course, the girl has no reputation.'

Pablo looked almost relieved to see that Gregor had returned, a *boleadora* in his hand. Mrs. Comber pounced upon it.

'Now isn't that cute! Look at all that tooling on the leather. And the silver studs!'

Marint laughed. 'This isn't a real one — it's just for decoration! The ones *vaqueros* use are plain strips of twisted hide — nothing ornamental.'

'Now let me see — I've never handled one before — three strips of leather, each with a weight on one end, and the three free ends joined together. You hold one ball — "

' — and swing the *boleadora* over your head. Then release it — but not in here — a sitting chandelier is not a fair quarry.

Now she was standing close to him, laughing at his joke. Her husband came up and examined the *boleadora*.

'Say, that's a fine one! I guess that's used for dancing, not hunting, eh?'

Marint laughed again. 'Perhaps it's the same thing.'

'Oh, General Marint!' Mrs. Comber protested. 'All these hints — it just isn't fair. And according to Don Pablo I shan't see the dance you were going to tell us about — he says that no one here would ever have done it. I sure am disappointed.'

247

'With all respect, I consider Señor de Zurga is being unrealistic. It's true it's not often danced in the ballroom. But it could be.'

Pablo was stung into contradiction. 'It could not, General Marint. It would be most improper!'

'The same thing was said in Europe of the waltz, when it was first introduced,' Marint answered calmly.

Pablo pursed up his lips and his frown deepened. To those around, it forecast that the exchange might become interesting again. Heads were turning, people were moving nearer, smiles were being slyly smothered.

Marint stood, dangling the *boleadora* from one hand, and went on as blandly as before.

'In Europe, when polite young ladies were not allowed to dance the waltz in public, they contrived to practise it in private. Do you seriously assert that no single girl of good birth has ever tried the *vaqueros'* dance, that your young bloods don't practise it at every opportunity, and that the married women of your acquaintance have only danced it with their husbands at a private party as a daring little joke?'

Pablo, looking more furious than before, faced Marint squarely. 'I think you are a blackguard to suggest otherwise!'

Mrs. Comber was looking bewildered. 'But, General Marint, what's so special about it? Is it — shocking?'

'Shocking? It doesn't shock me. But I've been a *vaquero*.'

'And you've danced it?'

'Of course I've danced it! Dozens of times — with nice girls — and I'm a polygamist as a result.'

There was more laughter, their audience was increasing minute by minute. To many this was a piece of entertainment they had not expected, and they did not intend to miss any of it. A few heads turned when music began to sound from the ballroom; Mrs. Comber raised a cry of questioning delight.

'Oh, what are they playing?'

Marint was smiling as if with inward satisfaction. 'By a strange coincidence it is *El Baile de la Boleadora*.'

Pablo looked like thunder again, and snapped, 'But here,

Mrs. Comber, everyone will dance it as a tango.'

Doña Ana suddenly felt that there was an inevitability about the development of this abrasive discussion. She could almost believe that Marint had engineered the whole thing, that he wanted a showdown with Pablo, and that any excuse would do. But in public, at such a function? He could hardly have chosen any place where the sensation would be greater, the repercussions more widely felt.

Mrs. Comber's sharp voice pierced the murmurs and laughter. 'Won't anyone dance it like a *vaquero*?'

Now Marint was answering her. 'Unfortunately, Mrs. Comber, I cannot ask for a partner. In the circumstances the ladies here might well feel that, although it could be discourteous to refuse, it would be even more embarrassing to accept.'

Pablo's full mouth twisted into a sneer.

'I am glad you have some sense of decency, General Marint – enough not to ask a lady to risk her reputation in order to pander to your vanity! You say you have no wife, and presumably no *novia*. If you wanted to demonstrate your skill at this ill-bred and questionable amusement you should have brought your own partner – that is, if you could find anyone sufficiently lacking in modesty and morals! A mistress, perhaps?'

The crowd quietened, anticipating trouble. Ana could feel the tension building up. It was like someone tightening a guitar string too much, one waited nervously for it to snap. It was unlikely that Marint would allow Pablo's last remark to pass. But he still smiled.

'Whose would you suggest? Have you one to spare?'

Gasps from feminine throats were drowned in a roar of laughter. Pablo's face was suffused, he began to stutter, checked himself, and in the pause Marint continued smoothly.

'No? It seems I must resign myself to dancing in the conventional fashion.'

He glanced around, apparently casually, and Doña Ana saw his eyes and Elena's meet. Her own attention had been

249

concentrated on the two men, now she saw that Elena was pale and tense, her mouth set firmly. She was furious, resenting Pablo's attitude, longing for someone to show they considered Marint as good as any hidalgo. And if no one did? As his look rested on her decision flashed into her eyes. *Por Dios*, no! They must not do it! He must not ask her, for if he does, she will dance it with him — and that will be utter disaster. She will be finished in society, he must know that.

Elena's chin lifted as she faced him. 'I believe I promised you a dance, General Marint.'

He had played on Pablo, he had manoeuvred this. For what? He must know what she is doing. But it's not too late. If he's a gentleman he'll avoid her action, accept a later dance, anything rather than let her compromise herself in this way. Or is that what he wants? He couldn't be such a brigand — there won't be a house in our society in which she will be accepted, save mine.

He stepped up to Elena. 'You did, Señorita Moural.'

Madre de Dios, after all that Pablo had said, he is letting her do it. She is placing herself in his hands — what will he do with her? If marriage is not in his book, what then? Did he intend to make her his mistress?

The seconds were stretching out, in the dead silence everyone waited, and when the words came she knew that although Marint had engineered the situation Elena was making her choice freely and boldly. Her look challenged them all, her voice was clear and steady.

'It was this one, I believe. And I should prefer the correct dance, rather than a tango, if I can remember it.'

So that was it. She would go to the ballroom as Elena Moural, but she would leave the floor as Marint's woman. If he wanted the triumph of having an hidalgo mistress, in everyone's opinion it would be his.

He was bowing and offering Elena his arm. In spite of herself Doña Ana took a pace forward, hoping in desperation that a look from her might check him. He stared full at her. His eyes gleamed, like two dark topazes, but nothing could be read in them, nor was there any expression on the dark smooth-sculptured face. She had thought better of him — let her not be wrong.

He turned back to Elena, and spoke as she put her fingers on his sleeve. 'You are quite right. I am most fortunate. It was this dance. Shall we go?'

Elena and Gregor Marint were on the ballroom floor. He had stripped off his jacket — only Gregor could take off his coat to dance at a Presidential Ball and get away with it. And now as they stood facing each other the *boleadora* was swinging from his right hand. His look told Elena nothing, and his voice was quiet so that only she would hear.

'If you're saving my face you've gone far enough. We can tango.'

Her answer came low and fierce, though she had not considered her motive. 'I'm not saving your face. I didn't think you'd want that.'

'I don't. I want you.'

There was nothing she could say to that, so she raised her arms, ready for the dance. He moved a few steps away, swinging the *boleadora*, testing the weight and feel of it. Then he came back to her, stepping in time to the beat of the music with the smoothness and precision of a stalking cat, stopping with his feet matching hers, standing so close that their bodies almost touched. All evening they had been without the slightest physical contact, save for the few moments when her hand lay on his sleeve; now her hunger at his nearness was almost unbearable. Then his hand moved.

She gasped as the thongs of the *boleadora* swept round her waist like a whiplash, and carried by the weight of the balls they jerked her against him, binding her body to his. With a flick of the fingers he locked the weights over each other so that the thongs could not unwind. He linked his hands behind his arched back, and she poised hers upon her hips. The dance began.

They moved together sinuously, in simple steps at first,

251

settling into complete accord. The couples on the floor thinned out as they saw what was happening; before long they would be dancing alone, everyone else would be watching. The orchestra was playing one of the songs of the pampa, the music rich with guitars, brilliant with trumpet notes, throbbing with the beat of drums. The dance had an insistent broken rhythm, and upon this rhythm the steps were woven, sweeping to and fro, halting, changing direction, growing more and more complicated.

The leather thongs were tight around her waist, ready to bite through her thin dress if she leaned against them. They made her keep close to her partner. Even had she wanted to she could not have avoided the contact of his body. In the tradition of the dance from the waist up they held themselves apart, so she, moving backwards, with arched spine must accept the intimacy of a male body pressed to hers. Somewhere within her tenseness melted into delight. She knew she not only acquiesced but rejoiced in it, that it eased in part her months'-old longing for Gregor.

Around her the room swung in a blur of light and colour, pink faces, brown faces, bright dresses, black suits, with glow of gold and flash of diamantine drops, all confused and blended into unreality. But Gregor was real. Strong and lithe and powerful his legs moved against hers, her hips were held against his loins, before her his broad shoulders and muscular chest were like a bulwark. There was music in her ears and above her was Gregor's face. His hazel eyes flecked with brown, his lips, were beginning to smile.

'Well, it's one way to get you alone.'

Her eyelids flicked up in surprise. She did not answer, forcing her mind to concentrate on the dance. But the steps she had often watched came easily to her memory now, and her thoughts flowed on. The dance was sensual and unin-hibited, like the *vaqueros* who created it. Gregor knew that, and didn't care. He saw no reason to be ashamed of it, although it was the dance of a man hunting a woman, a dance of fierce desire bent on capture and fulfilment. He wanted her.

252

He had said so; the dance said so.

Their bodies swayed together. His steps became more vigorous, his narrow loins were pressed harder against her, as if exulting in his dominance he was demanding from her an equal delight in surrender. She gave herself without reserve to the intimate passion of the dance, knowing it to be a near pre-figuring of the preliminary rites of love.

'It's not enough.'

His voice cut through her thoughts, but she did not dare to be sure of his meaning.

'What then?' she whispered.

His answer was broken by the rhythm of the dance, his voice low and thick with suppressed emotion.

'After this, come with me. Will you?'

Her body swung around his, he was the axis of her world, without him all meaning, all cohesion would be lost.

'Yes.'

The people watching saw his white teeth flash as he smiled, saw the two figures sweep around as if driven by mutual desire, till at the last moment, in a flurry of guitar notes, they rocked to a halt.

Gregor was untying the *boleadora*, they were surrounded by people laughing and applauding, it was for a short while a glorious triumphant confusion. Someone was holding Gregor's dinner jacket for him to put on; Aunt Ana was beside her, giving her her fan and evening bag, smiling warmly and pressing her hand. The *Norte-Americanos* were loud in their praises, Gregor's supporters were warm in their approval.

All the fuss beforehand seemed totally unnecessary, no one was shocked or offended. Now Gregor was making a way through the crowd and she was following. He was laughing and calling back answers to the remarks which were being tossed at them over the heads of the men and women who were hemming them in. She was laughing too, riding high on a tide of elation, exhilarated by the knowledge of Gregor's need of her.

Then he turned and spoke quietly to her. 'You have a

reception committee.'

The people around them fell back, and she saw what he meant. Riquezan hidalgo society had banded together: in front of and to one side of her was a solid mass of rigid figures and disapproving faces, silent, unsmiling, cold-eyed and hostile. She had broken their code and there was no doubt about their reaction. Raddled faces thick with powder and paint were masks of scorn and disgust; smooth young faces were contemptuous; old and young the men were sneering, out-raged, angry and in some way predatory. Elena felt all their eyes upon her, and in such a concerted gaze there was more than animosity and aversion.

It was her own fault. She should have realized the full significance of the dance, innocence was no excuse. She knew it was forbidden to single girls of her class, even at private parties – and she had danced it with a man outside their society at a public occasion – she might as well have embraced him in the middle of the Plaza Colón! Now she must take the consequences. Social ostracism was inevitable.

She forced herself to walk steadily on, with Gregor now beside her. As they reached the wall of silent, staring figures there was a click and a slight movement. A fan had opened. Then behind it the owner remarked to her neighbour in a hissing whisper, 'Disgraceful! Her father would never have allowed it!'

In the expectant hush it was audible to everyone. Next a soft whirr; behind this fan the woman addressed replied, 'She seems determined to shame her family.'

Ahead of her as she moved fans clicked and rustled, one after the other. Behind each in turn some comment was passed, making an intentional catalogue of her misdeeds. She tried not to hear them, but they could not be ignored. It was like running the gauntlet, with words instead of blows, and each word struck and stung.

'So ungrateful – she persistently refused him – the arrangements had to be cancelled – '

'And such an excellent match – '

'Particularly for a girl in her position — '

'Now she's trying to rob her own mother of some of her property — '

'She has taken up with a half-breed girl and says she's her sister-in-law!'

'What a tale! But she seems to have a partiality for that sort of person — '

As the woman spoke, the men looked. Elena hardly knew which was worse, because she could see only too plainly behind the enmity, the appraisal that lurked in every eye. She knew what they were thinking, and felt physically sick. They're wondering whether I've slept with him, she thought, and if not, whether he'll seduce me tonight.

And now they were approaching the de Zurgas. Her mother, haughty and implacable; Maddalena was scandalously amused; and Enrique, as ever taking his cue from his father, seemed shocked and disgusted. Concha, sneering, was loftily affronted — and there was Manuel. Manuel was the only one not to show enmity, and he stared at her calmly with such a naked calculation of the extent of Gregor's conquest that she wanted to cry out her protesting virginity. Next was Pablo, scowling and grim, and Carlos. Carlos, she saw, was drunk.

She thought she was going to be able to pass them without speech or incident. She was nearly abreast of them when Cristina said, 'If she wants to behave like a little whore, for heaven's sake let her! She's not fit for our family.'

Pablo's voice was urgent in her ear. 'You see what people think! You've got to prove them wrong — then we can — '

She took a deep breath and her own voice rang out crisp with pride. 'I'll prove nothing! They can think what they like. I've finished with the lot of you! Gregor, I wish to leave. Will you escort me?'

He did not look at her. Suddenly Colonel Córdoba's voice was heard: 'Escort the lady, Gregor. This is my job. Any more of this and I class it as a public disturbance!'

Gregor nodded, then with a sharp gesture he made a passage for her. Side by side they walked out of the great room, through the next, out of the confusion, the heat, the smell of people and perfume and wine, into the marble-floored vestibule where someone put her wrap about her shoulders, and on into the cool purple and gold of the lamp-lit night.

Outside in the dark flash-bulbs exploded, searing white. I've had all this before, she thought, as she hurried beside Gregor down the steps. He was parrying questions, fending off journalists and photographers.

'The Señorita and I have business to discuss . . .'
' . . . about land and horses, naturally . . . ' ' – but I consider those very serious subjects!' And then to her, 'We'll walk.'

When the last pursuer had given up he grinned and said, 'That fooled them. If we'd taken a cab they'd have been listening for the place. It's not far, anyway.'

No, it's not far, she thought, not far from the Presidential Palace to his flat. Now the empty feeling which comes with nerves swept over her. She tried not to think of anything. If she did she would wonder what was going to happen. But didn't she know? *Madre de Dios,* what a fool she was. Every day women were giving themselves to men, it couldn't be so embarrassing, so difficult – if only she knew something about it.

'What did Colonel Córdoba mean?' she asked. 'About a public disturbance?'

Gregor chuckled. 'He meant that if the de Zurgas gave any more trouble they'd spend the night in the cooler.'

'In the – spend the night in *prison*?'

'Yes. Ramón would do it, too.'

He became serious again. 'You had to make your own decision – you knew that. I couldn't help you. But you've made the break. From now on it will be different.'

'Different?'

'Yes. You've given a lead. There will be other girls fighting against the old conventions. They will join you.'

She recalled the scene at the Presidential Palace; it had been nerve-racking, disgraceful. She was trembling again, she felt utterly wretched. The air struck cold after the heated rooms, and she pulled her wrap closer around her, shivering. Tears were pricking her eyelids.

Gregor glanced down at her. 'If it was worth doing you've nothing to cry over,' he said brusquely. 'If you regret it you'd better go back — you'll catch old de Zurga if you hurry.'

She blinked her tears back and rage supplanted self-pity. 'I don't regret it. I hate the lot of them and all they stand for. They're not worth a peso — except Aunt Ana, of course.'

'Agreed! I'll take you back to her house — when we've had our talk.'

She saw the ghost of a smile on his lips. Perhaps he had been harsh with her on purpose. Sympathy would have encouraged the tears to flow, and that would have been disastrous. An hidalga did not cry in the street. An hidalga did not take a man's arm in the street either — not at her age, unless he was her father, brother, or husband, which meant that Gregor was setting the pace and she was being forced into a trot to keep up with him.

'Don't walk so fast!'

'Sorry!' He slackened his pace. 'It's those heels of yours — and my impatience.'

Dios! Her heart thudded again. What was going to happen when they reached his flat? They could talk now, without going there. 'I want you', he had said. 'Come with me.' She must go and take the consequences. If she tried to draw back now she would ruin everything.

They were turning into a quiet road. She recognized the street — they were almost there. Their steps were ringing on the paving. Now there were not many passers-by. She knew that each one approaching looked at herself and Gregor curiously, and when they had passed she could hear their footsteps falter as they turned to stare after them. Gregor looked completely unconcerned. She wished fervently that she could be as casual about it.

This was the house. Her heart was beating fast. Without a word Gregor opened the outer door and held it for her. They were in the hall; a porter was sitting in one corner; she hoped he was asleep. They reached the lift; they were inside; they were whirring up, clanging to a halt; they were out, and had reached Gregor's door.

He found his keys and let them in; the place was in darkness. Switching on lights, opening and shutting doors, and still in silence, he showed her into his living-room. She heard that door also close.

The room had not changed since she first saw it. She remembered its look of unfashionable comfort; the big shabby chairs, the shelves of books, the tidy desk-table, the military prints and the picture of horsemen on the pampa.

She stood in the middle of the room, pretending to glance about her, not daring to move or speak. The difficulty of her situation appalled her. If he only wanted her for a night – if he soon tired of her, what would she do? Where could she go?

He came round to face her and they stood looking at each other. He was serious, thoughtful. She felt his hands on her shoulders taking her wrap. He put it on a chair and she placed her bag, her fan, her gloves precisely upon it.

As she straightened, his hands clasped her bare arms and drew her towards him. Suddenly the tension melted from her, she swayed and found herself in his arms. He began to kiss her. She was clutching his jacket; beneath the smooth stuff she could feel the remembered hardness of muscle and firm flesh. She held herself close to him as he kissed her repeatedly.

'It's been so long – so long – ' he muttered.

'I've missed you,' she whispered.

It was childish, banal, but it didn't matter. He gave a little pleased laugh and his arms tightened around her.

'I had to know you trusted me. So you do?'

'Of course. I always have!'

Even as she spoke she knew it wasn't quite true. She had not trusted him enough. All the little rumours she had heard or read had stuck in her mind like burrs in a blanket, and it had been a struggle to clear her brain of them. But she must trust his feeling for her – had he not pushed himself to the

258

verge of death for her sake? Remorse for her doubts struck her and her eyes filled with tears.

'Don't cry, *querida,* don't cry. I want you to be happy,' he murmured gently, and his hand stroked her hair.

He was so male, so strong, and yet could be so tender. It struck her to the heart. Her arms slid over his shoulders and around his neck. At this simple gesture of affection his face lit up, his eyes shone, a smile creased his cheek. His masculinity flowed over her like a wave as he set his lips on hers again, kissing her firmly, strongly. She responded to him without reserve.

His mouth, a warm and living thing, began to move, parting her lips, and sensuous tremors ran through her. She was almost lying in his arms, held as if bound to him from head to foot; she was throbbing in every limb, ecstatic, limp with longing. His hands began to caress her.

She did not prevent him, but rested against him as he stroked the curve of thigh and buttock and hip. His hand moved slowly, purposefully, as if learning every curve and plane of her body. Would he understand that she knew nothing?

She stayed with her eyes closed, waiting. The hand on her back slid round her shoulders, across and down in a movement surprisingly gentle, deliberately sensuous. Emotion rose within her.

'This is how it must be,' he murmured, and began to kiss her throat. 'I want everything.'

I love you, Gregor, her heart was saying, but the words would not come, he had said, 'I want', not 'I love', and she was still shy of telling him. He drew her closer to him.

'*Amorcita mia*, you're all I've ever wanted in a woman.'

'I'm glad . . . '

'I thought you were glad before – but I didn't convince you – '

A fierce compulsion was rising from the depths of her being, crying out for satisfaction; she acknowledged it, and knew for the first time that her passion could equal his. She had cut loose from her old ties and come to him; her surrender to be of any value must be complete.

'Gregor, I belong to you,' she whispered.

Her pulses were throbbing madly, her heart was thudding, she tingled, melted, ached with love. For a long moment he held her.

'And I love you as I've never loved a woman. Ah, *chica*, why couldn't it be summer now!'

'Why summer?'

'Why? When it comes I'll show you . . . '

'Tell me, *querido*.'

He pressed his cheek to hers. 'Why – then we'll ride out together on the pampa, and spend days and nights in the open. When we've hobbled the horses and camped we'll lie bedded deep in grass, the smell of it in our nostrils mixed with the smoke from the wood fire. All night you'll lie in my arms.'

'As close as this . . . '

'No, closer! In the moonlight I'll cover you with kisses. You will belong to me, flesh of my flesh, bone of my bone. We'll make love, then sleep till dawn, wrapped in the same poncho . . . '

She smiled at him, tenderly, with the eyes of love.

'Gregor *mío*, you want me – and I'm here – I can belong to you without waiting.'

Gregor Marint, looking down at the girl in his arms, saw that she was more beautiful than she had ever been. The impossible had happened, the love which had eluded him all his life had come to him at last.

'Tell me, *querido*, shall I stay?'

There should be only one answer to that question, for he was eager, racked with passion. Yet for her everything must be perfect, and this was not the time nor the place. He had been given proof of love, and with that he was strangely, gloriously content.

'I want you – *Dios*, how I want you! But we shall be married soon, *Hija de Valdoro*. I can wait.'